RICHARD ANTHONY PROCTOR

A LIBRARY OF UNIVERSAL LITERATURE

IN FOUR PARTS

Comprising Science, Biography, Fiction
and the Great Orations

PART ONE—SCIENCE

OTHER WORLDS THAN OURS

BY

RICHARD A. PROCTOR, B.A., F.R.A.S.

NEW YORK
P. F. COLLIER AND SON
· MCMI ·
14

A LIBRARY OF
UNIVERSAL LITERATURE

SCIENCE

VOLUME FOURTEEN

"Lo, these are parts of His ways: but how little a portion is heard of Him? the thunder of His power who can understand?" —JOB xxvi. 14.

CONTENTS

ILLUSTRATIONS

PREFACE

THE general purpose I have had in view in writing the present treatise will be gathered from the introductory pages; but I wish to offer here a few remarks on certain points of detail.

It will be seen that, on many of the subjects dealt with in this work, I have propounded views which differ from those usually accepted. I have not done this from any love of novelty, nor from any desire to attract attention by *bizarre* or fanciful theories. Each of the new views here presented has been the result of a careful study of the subject dealt with, and I have searched as anxiously for considerations opposed to any novel theory as for arguments in its favor. If others should be more successful than I have been in finding reasons for rejecting any of my views, I shall be ready to abandon them without regret. I trust I am free from that weakness which forces a man to regard every theory he has once advocated as a matter to be defended at all hazards. No weakness more mischievously affects the work of the student of science. As Faraday said, "Truth should be the primary object of the philosopher"; and this can never be the case if, where he imagines he holds a theory, the theory has in truth possession of *him*.

Some among my readers will recognize, in the views here presented, the growth of ideas which I have dealt with consecutively, with more or less fulness, in the pages of several quarterly, monthly, and weekly serials, and in one of our leading daily newspapers. I refer to this, because it has happened to me several times lately to be accused of plagiarism, when I have had occasion, in developing fresh ideas on a subject, to repeat statements which (unknown of course to my accusers) had proceeded from my own pen. It is not often one is accused of stealing one's own ideas, but that is a pleasure I have more than once been enabled to enjoy of late, and I here present my compliments to those who (anonymously or otherwise) have afforded me that luxury.

Wherever it has been in accordance with the custom of any journal, however, I have always written under my own name.

Since the manuscript of this work was placed in

the printers' hands, I have obtained fresh evidence
on some of the theories dealt with in the following
pages.

One of the most surprising phenomena ever witnessed by the telescopist—a phenomenon I had read
of long since, but had not thought of in connection
with my subject—seems to me to afford stronger evidence than any adduced in the text, in favor of my
theory that the major planets are subsidiary suns
supplying heat (if not a minute proportion of light
even) to their satellites. I refer to the observation
made by Admiral Smyth, that on one occasion the
second satellite of Jupiter, twelve minutes after entering on the disk of the planet, was seen *outside the
limb*, "where it remained four minutes, and then suddenly vanished." Two other equally competent observers, Maclear and Pearson, witnessed the same
phenomenon. "Here," says Webb, "explanation is
set at defiance." But it is precisely where explanation seems set at defiance that the true student of
Nature is most hopeful of gaining instruction. The
observation is very startling, it is true; and the
explanation may be expected to be also surprising.
But I think it is not far to seek. The satellite cannot
have retraced its course; Jupiter cannot have shifted
his place; our atmosphere cannot be in question:
surely, when all these explanations are eliminated,

our task is rendered easier instead of more difficult. A change of shape in Jupiter, corresponding to that which I have endeavored to exhibit as explaining Saturn's occasional assumption of the square-shouldered aspect, would obviously account for the phenomenon. We know that Schröter suspected an apparent flattening of portions of Jupiter's outline. Here we have an effective confirmation of that long-doubted observation. If we consider the matter rightly, the observation made simultaneously by Smyth, Maclear, and Pearson, makes that view all but certain which in the text I have presented only as a highly-probable hypothesis.

In preparing the Maps for my new Atlas (now nearly ready), I have detected signs of systematic aggregation among stars visible to the naked eye, which seem to me to place beyond all question the fact that Sir William Herschel adopted an erroneous hypothesis as the basis of his system of star-gauging. The fact that about one-third of the lucid stars are collected in a region having the greater Magellanic Cloud nearly in its centre, and covering less than one-sixth of the heavens, has never yet, so far as I am aware, been noticed. Supplemented by other facts, detected during the work of transferring the stars of the British Association Catalogue to my Maps, the existence of this rich region around the

Nubeculæ disposes at once of the hypothesis of a generally uniform distribution within the sidereal system. I shall be enabled, by Mr. Brothers's kindness, to illustrate my Lecture on the Stars at the Royal Institution on May 6th by means of photographs of the Maps which thus conclusively (at least in my opinion) establish the theory that there exist special and discernible laws of aggregation among the lucid stars.

I may add in this place that it is not the case, as has been recently asserted, that my theories respecting the sidereal system have been founded on the discovery that certain nebulæ are gaseous. That discovery, so far from being opposed to the theories of Sir William Herschel, afforded most striking evidence of his wonderful reasoning powers, since he had been led to express his firm conviction that many nebulæ are gaseous, had confidently asserted that the Orion nebula is so, and had even anticipated the discovery of the variability of the irregular nebulæ, recently effected by Le Sueur of Melbourne.

My theory respecting the sidereal system has been based on the signs of systematic aggregation among the lucid stars, and of a more intimate association of those stars with the Milky Way than could be expected were Sir William Herschel's fundamental the-

ory correct. My first paper on the subject, in the
Intellectual Observer for August, 1867, was entitled
"Notes on Star-Streams"; and it was only while
inquiring into the nature of stellar aggregation that
I was led to notice the laws of nebular distribution, and so to inquire into the relations between
stars and nebulæ. I take this opportunity of
thanking my kind friend, the editor of the *Intellectual Observer and Student*, for the exceptional
liberality with which he has found a place for
views professedly opposed to generally - received
opinions.

The theory brought forward in the chapter on
Meteors and Comets is not altogether new. The
general idea on which it is grounded has been dealt
with by Mayer and Thompson, while the relation
between the motions of discrete bodies and the formation of systems of orbs has been dealt with by Sir
John Herschel, in considering his father's hypotheses
respecting the nebulæ. That idea, however, presented itself independently to my mind when I was
writing my treatise on Saturn (at which time my acquaintance with scientific literature was very limited
indeed), and is definitely stated in Note B of the
Appendix to that work. The line of reasoning is
wholly new, I believe, by which I have endeavored
to show that those peculiarities of the solar system

which have hitherto been regarded as affording the strongest objection to the hypothesis of development may be regarded as in reality the direct result of the processes by which the solar system has reached its present condition. In the preface to my treatise on Saturn I touched on the possibility that some such explanation of those peculiarities might be found, remarking that in the rings of Saturn astronomers may one day recognize the action of the processes by which the solar system has attained its present state.

In the chapter on the Sun I have entered at some length into the subject of the solar corona, partly because that subject is full of interest in view of the approaching total solar eclipse visible in the south of Europe, and partly because I have seen with regret that an erroneous theory of the corona has been recently promulgated, which seems likely at the present conjuncture to affect mischievously the progress of research into this interesting question of solar physics.

I have heard with much pleasure that the Astronomer Royal, at the last meeting of the Astronomical Society, altogether repudiated any share in starting this theory. Although I had seen his name associated with it, I had always thought it incredible that a mathematician so skilful and clear-sighted should have advanced or adopted so ill-considered a hypothesis.

I here tender my best thanks to Mr. Brothers, F.R.A.S., for his careful revision of the proof-sheets, and the detection of more than one error which had escaped my scrutiny.

RICHARD A. PROCTOR.

LONDON, *April* 12, 1870.

THE PLURALITY OF WORLDS

OTHER WORLDS THAN OURS

INTRODUCTION

ASTRONOMY and Geology owe much of their charm to the fact that they suggest thoughts of other forms of life than those with which we are familiar. Geology teaches us of days when this earth was peopled with strange creatures such as now are not found upon its surface. We turn our thoughts to the epochs when those monsters throve and multiplied, and picture to ourselves the appearance which our earth then presented. Strange forms of vegetation clothe the scene which the mind's eye dwells upon. The air is heavily laden with moisture to nourish the abundant flora; hideous reptiles crawl over their slimy domain, battling with each other or with the denizens of the forest; huge batlike creatures sweep through the dusky twilight which constituted the primeval day; weird monsters pursue their prey amid the ocean depths: and we forget, as we dwell upon the strange forms which existed in those long past ages, that the scene now presented by the earth is no less wonderful, and that the

(17)

records of our time may perhaps seem one day as perplexing as we now find those of the geological eras.

Astronomy has a kindred charm. We cannot indeed examine the actual substance of living creatures existing upon other celestial bodies; we cannot even picture to ourselves their appearance or qualities; and only in a few instances can we even form any conception of the conditions under which they live. But we see proofs on all sides that, besides the world on which we live, other worlds exist as well cared for and as nobly planned. Nay, we see globes by the side of which our earth would seem but as a tiny speck; we trace these globes as they sweep with stately motion on their appointed courses; we watch the return of day on the broad expanse of their surface; and we see systems of satellites which are suspended as lights for their nocturnal skies. We further find that our sun is matched by a thousand thousand suns amid the immeasurable depths of space; and the mind's eye pictures other worlds like those which course around the sun, travelling in stately orbits around his fellow-luminaries.

Long, however, before the wonders of modern astronomy had been revealed to us, men of inquiring minds seem to have been led, as by an irresistible instinct, to examine into the resemblance which may exist between our world and other worlds surrounding it on every hand. It has not been the mere fanciful theorizer who has discussed such questions, but men of the highest eminence in science. In long past ages Anaximander and Pythagoras studied the subject of other worlds than ours; later, such men as Huyghens, Galileo, and Newton have dwelt upon the same interesting theme; while, in our own day, Whewell and Brewster have employed their scientific and dialectic skill in defending rival theories upon the subject.

Undoubtedly a large share of the interest with which the question of other worlds than ours has been regarded, is due to the fact that, as the science of astronomy has progressed, the subject has continually presented itself under new aspects. The question, in fact, is one of those which are ever new and ever old. It has all the charm belonging to subjects which men in all ages have delighted to discuss, while it is associated in the most intimate manner with the progress of modern science. With what a charm of novelty, for instance, the discussion between Whewell and Brewster invested the subject! No doubt a large portion of that charm was due to the personal qualities of the two disputants. Yet, despite the skill with which each of them presented the arguments belonging to his own side of the controversy, few could have read with any interest a discussion on a subject so well worn, had it not been that the arguments were drawn from the discoveries which had recently been made by astronomers. Nor was it uninteresting to notice how these discoveries at once seemed to acquire a new interest when they were associated with the subject of life in other worlds. Facts which had attracted little notice at the time of their discovery at once assumed importance, when it was seen how they bore on the rival views which Whewell and Brewster were enforcing. The interest with which the public regard many of these discoveries may, indeed, be said to date from the controversy between those eminent men.

No very long interval, if we count by years, has elapsed since the "Plurality of Worlds" and "More Worlds than One" were written. Yet so rapidly has science progressed, that already the subject of life in other worlds has assumed a new aspect. Arguments which were hypothetical thirty years ago have either become certainties or been disproved. Doubtful points have been cleared up; a new meaning has been found even in those facts which were well known to both the disputants; and lastly, a new mode of research has been devised, which has not only revealed a number of surprising facts, but promises to work yet greater marvels in the years which are to come.

One is thus invited to discuss anew a subject which but a few years since seemed thoroughly sifted by the inquiries of the two eminent philosophers I have named. We stand in a position much more favorable for the formation of just views than that from which Whewell and Brewster surveyed the planetary and stellar systems. Never, since men first explored the celestial depths, has a series of more startling discoveries rewarded the labors of astronomers and physicists than during the past few years. Unhoped-for revelations have been made on every side. Analogies the most interesting have brought the distant orbs of heaven into close relationship with our own earth, or with the central luminary of the planetary scheme. And a lesson has been taught us which bears even more significantly on our views respecting the existence of other worlds: we have learned to recognize within the solar system, and within the wondrous galaxy of which our sun is a constituent orb, a variety of structure and a complexity of detail, of which but a few years ago astronomers had formed but the most inadequate conceptions.

My object, then, in the pages which follow, is not solely to establish the thesis that there are other worlds than ours, but to present, in a new and I hope interesting light, the marvellous discoveries which have rewarded recent scientific researches. Judged merely according to their direct significance, these discoveries are well calculated to excite our admiration for the wonderful works of God in His universe, and for the far-reaching scope of the mental powers which He has given to His creature Man. But it is when we consider recent discoveries in their relation to the existence of other worlds, when we attempt to form a conception of the immense varieties of the forms of life corresponding to the innumerable varieties of cosmical structure disclosed by modern researches, that we recognize the full significance of those discoveries. Although the growth of our knowledge is ever accompanied by a proportional growth of our estimate of the unknown, we seem already entitled to say that we have

> Come on that which is, and caught
> The deep pulsations of the world,
> Æonian music, measuring out
>   The steps of time.

CHAPTER I

WHAT OUR EARTH TEACHES US

BEFORE proceeding to consider the various circumstances under which the worlds or systems which surround us appear to subsist, it may be well to inquire how far we have reason to conclude, from the consideration of our own earth and its inhabitants, that the Creator has designed the orbs which exist throughout space for the support of living creatures.

It would not be just to argue directly from the fact that the earth is inhabited to the conclusion that the other planets are inhabited also, nor thence to the conclusion that other stars have, like our sun, their attendant worlds, peopled with various forms of life. An analogy founded on a single instance has no logical force. And it is doubtful whether we have not, in the moon, an instance which would as effectually serve to support a directly opposite conclusion. It seems all but certain, as we shall presently have occasion to show, that no part of the moon's globe is inhabited by living creatures. Certainly she is inhabited by none which bear the least resemblance to those existing on our earth. Thus it might fairly be urged that, since one of the two orbs respecting which we know most appears to be unin- habited, there remains no probable argument in favor of the view that other orbs besides our earth are the abode of living creatures.

Yet the earth in reality supplies an argument of great force, when we consider the evidence she pre- sents in another light. The mere fact that this world is inhabited is, as we have seen, little; but we shall find that the way in which life is distributed over the earth's surface is full of significance.

If we range over the earth, from the arctic regions to the torrid zone, we find that none of the peculiari- ties which mark the several regions of our globe suf- fice to banish life from its surface. In the bitter cold within the arctic circles, with their strange alter- nations of long summer days and long winter nights, their frozen seas, perennial ice, and scanty vegeta- tion, life flourishes in a hundred various forms. On the other hand, the torrid zone, with its blazing heat, its long-continued droughts, its strange absence of true seasonal changes, and its trying alternations of oppressive calms and fiercely-raging hurricanes, nourishes even more numerous and more various forms of life than either of the great temperate zones. Around mountain summits as in the depths of the most secluded valleys, in mid-ocean as in the arid desert, in the air as beneath the surface of the earth, we find myriad forms of life.

But this is far from being all. Various as are the

physical habitudes which we encounter as we travel over the surface of our globe, we are able to trace the existence of other varieties even more remarkable. The geologist has been able to turn back a few leaves of the earth's past history, and, though the pages have been defaced and mutilated by Time's unsparing hand, he is yet able to read in them of many strange vicissitudes to which the continents and oceans of our globe have been exposed. But, far back as he can trace the earth's history, and already he counts her age by millions of years,[1] he finds no evidence of an epoch when life was absent from her surface. Nay, if he reads aright the mysterious lesson which the blurred letters teach him, he is led to believe that, at the most distant epoch to which his researches have extended, there was the same wonderful variety in the forms of life as at the present day. He can, indeed, find the scattered remains of only a few of those old-world creatures; but he recognizes, in those which have been preserved, the clearest evidence that thousands of others

---

[1] The results of the recent deep-sea dredging expeditions, though they have an obvious bearing on the question of the relative ages of the various strata of our earth, do not appreciably affect our estimate of the range of time during which this world has been the abode of living creatures. We can no longer assume that adjacent rocks which differ in character are necessarily different in age: but we have enough evidence, from superimposed strata, to prove the enormous antiquity of the earlier formations. The researches of Dr. Carpenter and his fellow-workers have a most important bearing, however, on the subject of the present chapter, and supply a more forceful analogy, perhaps, than any dwelt on in the text, in favor of the view that, under the widest varieties of condition, Nature may be most prodigal of life.

must have existed around them. He knows that, of a million creatures now existing, scarcely one will leave to future ages any record of its existence; he sees whole races vanishing from the earth, leaving no trace behind them; and he is thus able to form an estimate of the enormous extent by which the creatures and races of which he can learn *nothing* must have outnumbered those whose scattered remains attest their former existence upon the earth.

Here, then, we have analogies which there is no mistaking. We see that not only is Nature careful to fill all available space with living forms, but that no time over which our researches extend has found her less prodigal of life. We see that, within very wide limits, she has a singular power of adapting living creatures to the circumstances which surround them. Nor is this lesson affected—like the general lesson drawn from the mere fact of the earth's being inhabited—by anything we can learn from the aspect of our satellite. For the arguments against the presence of living creatures on the moon are founded on the evidence we have that the physical habitudes of that orb are outside the limits—wide as they seem to be—within which Nature can effect the adaptation we have spoken of.

In fact, if we consider rightly, the argument which has been drawn from the moon's presumed unfitness to be the abode of living creatures is so founded on terrestrial analogies as to leave the contrary argument unaffected. We have to assume that the argument drawn from the analogy of the earth is forceful before we can form any opinion at all respecting the moon's habitability. And, in any case, no argument can be drawn from the moon's unfitness for the support of life, against the view that, where orbs fit for the support of life exist, there Nature has provided such classes of living creatures as are adapted to the special habitudes of those orbs.

The moon teaches us, however, that the Creator has not intended all the celestial bodies to be at all times habitable. The sun also teaches the same lesson. And it is necessary that we should consider how far the evidence presented by our own earth may serve to elucidate this teaching. We shall see, as we proceed, that terrestrial analogies afford a very sure guide in the midst of many perplexities which the study of the worlds around us presents to our contemplation.

Let us trace out the various degrees of fitness or unfitness for the support of particular forms of life, which we recognize in various regions of our earth.

Often, where there exists so slight a difference between two regions of the earth that, to ordinary observation, it would appear that the forms of life existing in one should be well adapted to the other also, we yet find that this is not the case. Some minute peculiarity of soil, or climate, or vegetation, will render one region absolutely uninhabitable by a race which lives and thrives in the other. Darwin mentions several instances in which an apparently insignificant change in the circumstances under which a particular race has thriven, and sometimes a change which does not, at first sight, appear to be in the least connected with the well-being of the race, has led to its gradual disappearance. And it seems demonstrated that even the slow processes of change to which every part of the earth is subjected would suffice to destroy a number of the races now subsisting on its surface, were the characteristics of those races unalterable. But, as the physical habitudes of their abode slowly change, the various races of living creatures slowly change also, so as to adapt themselves continually to the varying circumstances under which they live.

The lesson taught us by this peculiarity is very obvious. On the one hand, we see that it would be by no means sufficient to indicate a general resemblance between the physical habitudes of our earth and those of some far-distant planet, in order to prove that that planet is the abode of living creatures resembling those on our own earth. But, on the other hand, we are taught that the existence of differences sufficient to render a distant planet an unsuitable abode for such creatures as we are familiar with cannot force upon us the conclusion that the planet is uninhabited. On the contrary, the circumstance we have been considering teaches us that such differences as would suffice to banish life of certain kinds are insufficient to banish life of all kinds, or even to render less abundant the forms of life which exist under those changed conditions.

And now we may proceed a step further. On our earth we find differences of climate and of physical habitudes generally, which are much more important than those hitherto dealt with. We see that not only would certain races perish in the long run, if removed from their own abode to other parts of the earth, but that, in some instances, the process of destruction would be very rapid indeed. If we were to remove the polar bears from their arctic fastnesses to tropical, or even to the warmer parts of temperate regions, a very few years would see the end of the whole race. The races inhabiting steppes and prairies would quickly perish, if removed to mountain regions. Those accustomed to a moisture laden air and abundant vegetation would not survive long if removed to the desert.

In some races, indeed, we find a power of enduring such changes which very far exceeds that possessed by other races. Those creatures, for example, which man has domesticated seem capable of enduring a variety of climate or of circumstances, which would destroy the seemingly more vigorous races which have not been subdued to the yoke of man.[1]

Even man himself, however, though he possesses in an unrivalled degree the power of enduring in safety the most complete change of climate, scene, and circumstances, is yet limited, in a certain sense,

---

[1] Humboldt tells us that "the pliability of the organization of those animals which man has subjected to his sway enables horses, cows, and other species of European origin to lead for a time an amphibious life, surrounded by crocodiles, water-serpents, and manatees. When the rivers return again to their beds, the horses roam in the savanna, which is then spread over with a fine odoriferous grass; and enjoy, as in their native climate, the renewed vegetation of spring."

in his power of migration. The Englishman, for
example, can endure the fiercest heat of the tropics
or the bitterest cold of arctic and antarctic regions.
But he cannot safely attempt to found true colonies
in every part of the earth's surface. Our country-
men in India must send their children to be reared
in England, if they wish them to grow up strong and
vigorous. There can be little doubt that if a thousand men and women from this country were to
settle in certain parts of India (not at any time inter-
marrying with the natives), the colony would have
disappeared within a couple of centuries.

Here we have a second degree of unfitness, according to which certain countries would quickly
become depopulated, if supplied with inhabitants
from certain other countries. We are taught the
same lesson as before, but in a more striking manner. We see that differences exist within the con-
fines of our own earth which render particular countries absolutely uninhabitable by particular races,
insomuch that, though the individual might survive,
the race itself would quickly perish. And we see,
on the other hand, that these countries are not uninhabited, or even less fully peopled with living creatures than seemingly more fortunate abodes.

Now, if some impassable barrier prevented the inhabitants of one country from visiting others, while
yet it was possible to learn something of the conditions prevailing in other regions, how readily the
conclusion might be reached, that some at least of
those inaccessible regions must be wholly uninhab-

ited, simply because their physical habitudes appeared unsuited to the wants of the only creatures with which the observer was familiar. Who would believe, for example, that men can live, and not only live but thrive and multiply, in the frost-bound regions within the Arctic Circle, if travellers had not visited the Esquimau races and witnessed the conditions under which they subsist? Again, if we knew nothing of India, and some one pictured to us the intense heat of the Indian sun, the strange alternations of weather which replace to the Indian the seasonal changes we are familiar with, and all the other circumstances which render tropical regions so different from our English home, who could believe that, amid those seemingly unendurable vicissitudes, there are races of men that thrive and multiply, even as our people in their temperate zone? [1]

Therefore, in examining the circumstances of other worlds than ours, it will not be sufficient to prove that certain orbs would obviously not be habitable by the races subsisting on the earth, in order to enforce the conclusion that no living creatures subsist at all upon their surface.

Yet another step further, however. There are re-

---

[1] Perhaps the most striking instance of man's power of living under circumstances seemingly the most unfavorable is to be found in the fact that, though the strongest traveller is affected seriously by the rarity of the air at great elevations, yet races of men live and thrive in Potosi, Bogota, and Quito, and—to use the words of a modern writer —that bull-fights should be possible at an elevation at which Saussure hardly had energy to consult his instruments, and where even his guides fainted as they tried to dig a small hole in the snow.

gions of the earth where the *individuals* of races belonging to other regions quickly perish. The air of our own England is death to many creatures. And, indeed, there is not a spot in the whole world which would not be fatal in a brief space to many animals and plants belonging to other regions. Yet each spot, though thus fatal to certain races, is inhabited by numbers of others, which live and thrive upon its surface.

Here, then, is our third lesson. We are taught, by the analogy of our earth, that it is not even sufficient to show that a planet would be an abode quickly fatal to all the living creatures subsisting on our globe, to prove that it is therefore uninhabited.

But we have yet a stronger argument to touch on. There are regions of our earth to which creatures from other regions cannot be removed without being immediately killed. The warm-blooded animal perishes if placed for a brief space under water. The fish perishes if placed for a brief space on the earth.[1] What could be more wonderful to us, were we not familiar with the fact, than that there are living creatures within the depths of that ocean, beneath whose surface we ourselves, and the land creatures we are familiar with, cannot remain alive many minutes? If fishes could reason, how could

---

[1] Perhaps the fact that there are certain kinds of fish which cannot only live out of water, but can travel across the dry land, or climb trees, affords an even more striking instance of Nature's power of adapting creatures to the circumstances which surround them.

they believe that creatures can live in comfort in that element which is death to them? Yet land and river and sea are alike peopled with living creatures, each race as well adapted as its fellows to the circumstances in which it is placed.

We are taught, then, yet another lesson. We see that, even though we could prove that every living creature on this earth would at once perish if removed to another orb, yet we cannot thence conclude that that orb is uninhabited. On the contrary, the lesson conveyed by our earth's analogy leads to the conclusion that many worlds may exist, abundantly supplied with living creatures of many different species, where yet every form of life upon our earth —bird, beast, or fish, reptile, insect, or animalcule— would perish in a few moments.[1]

There remains yet a last lesson to be drawn from terrestrial analogies. On the earth there are regions where no form of life exists or can exist. Within

---

[1] I might add, to the instances here cited, many others which seem even more striking. I have already referred to Dr. Carpenter's discovery, that in the depths of the Atlantic, where the pressure of the sea is so enormous that no ordinary instruments can resist its effects, where it had even been thought that no light can penetrate, there are myriads of living creatures having even organs of vision. We know, too, that in strong acids which would instantly kill bird, beast, fish, or insect placed within them, there exist and thrive minute creatures adapted by Nature to the strange conditions in which they are placed. Even in the bowels of the earth, and in the very neighborhood of active volcanoes, we find the volcano-fish existing in such countless thousands, that, when they are from time to time vomited forth by the erupting mountain, their bodies are strewn over enormous regions, and, as they putrefy beneath the sun's rays, spread pestilence and disease among the inhabitants of the neighboring districts.

the flaming crater of the volcano, or in the frozen heart of the iceberg, no living creature has its being. Yet even here Nature proves to us that the great end and aim of all her working is to afford scope and room for new forms of life, or to supply the wants of those which already exist. The volcano will die out, and the scene of its activity will one day become the abode of myriads of living creatures who would have perished in a moment in its consuming fires. The iceberg will melt, and its substance will once again be peopled with busy life. But this is little. It is the work of which volcano and iceberg are the signs which most significantly teaches us what is Nature's real aim. The volcano is the index of those busy subterranean forces which are remodelling the earth's frame, slowly changing the level of the land, making continents of oceans and oceans of continents, preserving and vivifying all things, while all things seem to suffer a gradual destruction. The iceberg, too, has its work in remodelling and fashioning the surface of new continents. But it exhibits also the action of Nature for the present benefit of the creatures which exist upon the earth. It acts an important part in the formation and maintenance of the system of oceanic circulation on which the welfare of land creatures and water creatures so largely depends. And so of a multitude of other phenomena, which appear at first sight significant rather of the destructive than of the life-preserving character of Nature. The tornado and the thunderstorm, the earthquake and the volcano—nay, even the dreaded returns of plague and pestilence, have each a more powerful influence by far toward the preservation than they have toward the destruction of life.

We see, then, that even when we can prove that an orb in space is so circumstanced that no life could by any possibility exist upon its surface; if it were the scene of a fierce and destructive turmoil, one moment of which would suffice to destroy every living creature now existing upon the earth; if its whole mass were heated to a degree a thousand-fold more intense than that of the fiercest heat we know of; if its surface were bound in a cold compared with which our arctic frosts would seem like tropical heat; or even if the most rapid alternation of these extremes took place upon and within it; even then we could not conclude that the principal purpose for which the Almighty had created it had not been the support of life, either in long-past ages or in ages yet to come. And lastly, though we could safely assert of any celestial object, that neither now, nor at any past or future time, could it serve as the abode of living creatures, yet we are led by terrestrial analogies to the conclusion that it has yet been created to support life in other ways. So that those very orbs, of which it seems safest to assert that they are, have ever been, and must ever remain uninhabited, speak to us, no less strongly than those which appear best suited for habitation, of the existence of other worlds than ours.

CHAPTER II

WHAT WE LEARN FROM THE SUN

I DO not propose to dwell in this chapter on the views which have been propounded respecting the sun's habitability. It is not merely that I regard those views as too *bizarre* and fanciful to find place in a serious consideration of the subject I am dealing with, nor that the progress of recent observation has rendered them utterly untenable, but that, in fact, they do not belong to what the sun teaches us. I wish to consider only the real evidence which the sun affords respecting the scheme of creation, to dwell upon the purposes which he subserves in the economy of the solar system, and thence to deduce a lesson respecting those other suns scattered throughout space, which we call the fixed stars.

Let us first endeavor to form adequate conceptions respecting the dimensions of the great central luminary of the solar system.

Let the reader consider a terrestrial globe three inches in diameter, and search out on that globe the tiny triangular speck which represents Great Britain.

Then let him endeavor to picture the town in which he lives as represented by the minutest pin-mark that could possibly be made upon this speck. He will then have formed some conception, though but an inadequate one, of the enormous dimensions of the earth's globe, compared with the scene in which his daily life is cast. Now, on the same scale, the sun would be represented by a globe about twice the height of an ordinary sitting-room. A room about twenty-six feet in length, and height, and breadth, would be required to contain the representation of the sun's globe on this scale, while the globe representing the earth could be placed in a moderately large goblet.

Such is the body which sways the motions of the solar system. The largest of his family, the giant Jupiter, though of dimensions which dwarf those of the earth or Venus almost to nothingness, would yet only be represented by a thirty-two inch globe, on the scale which gives to the sun the enormous volume I have spoken of. Saturn would have a diameter of about twenty-eight inches, his ring measuring about five feet in its extreme span. Uranus and Neptune would be little more than a foot in diameter, and all the minor planets would be less than the three-inch earth. It will thus be seen that the sun is a worthy centre of the great scheme he sways, even when we merely regard his dimensions.

The sun outweighs fully seven hundred and forty times the combined mass of all the planets which

circle around him, so that, when we regard the
energy of his attraction, we still find him a worthy
ruler of the planetary scheme.

But, after all, the enormous volume and mass of
the sun form the least important of his characteristics
as the ruling body of the solar system. It is when
we contemplate him as the source whence the supplies of heat and light required by our own world
and the other planets are plentifully bestowed, that
we see what is his chief office in the economy of
the planetary scheme.

Properly speaking, the physical constitution of the
sun only requires to be dealt with in such a work as
the present in so far as it is directly associated with
the sun's action upon the worlds around him, or as
it may bear on the question of the constitution of
those worlds. But the subject is so interesting, and
it would indeed be so difficult to draw a line of
demarcation between the facts which bear upon the
question of other worlds and those which do not,
that I may be permitted to enter at some length into
a consideration of the solar orb as modern physical
discoveries present it to our contemplation.

The study of solar physics may be said to have
commenced with the discovery of the sun spots, about
two hundred and sixty years ago. These spots were
presently found to traverse the solar disk in such a
way as to indicate that the sun turns upon an axis
once in about twenty-six days. Nor will this rotation
appear slow, when we remember that it implies a motion of the equatorial parts of the sun's surface at a

rate exceeding some seventy times the motion of our
swiftest express trains.

Next came the discovery that the solar spots are
not surface stains, but deep cavities in the solar substance. The changes of appearance presented by the
spots as they traverse the solar disk led Dr. Wilson
to form this theory so far back as 1779; but, strangely
enough, it is only in comparatively recent times that
the hypothesis has been finally established, since
even within the last ten years a theory was put forward which accounted satisfactorily for most of the
changes of appearance observed in the spots, by
supposing them to be due to solar clouds hanging
suspended at a considerable elevation above the true
photosphere.

Sir William Herschel, reasoning from terrestrial
analogies, was led to look on the spot-cavities as
apertures through a double layer of clouds. He
argued that, were the solar photosphere of any other
nature, it would be past comprehension that vast
openings should form in it, to remain open for
months before they close up again. Whether we
consider the enormous rapidity with which the spots
form and with which their figure changes, or the
length of time that many of them remain visible, we
find ourselves alike perplexed, unless we assume that
the solar photosphere resembles a bed of clouds.
Through a stratum of terrestrial clouds openings may
be formed by atmospheric disturbances, but while
undisturbed the clouds will retain any form once
impressed upon them, for a length of time corre-

sponding to the weeks and months during which the solar spots endure.

And because the solar spots present two distinct varieties of light, the faint penumbra and the dark umbra or nucleus, Herschel saw the necessity of assuming that there are two beds of clouds, the outer self-luminous and constituting the true solar photosphere, the inner reflecting the light received from the outer layer, and so shielding the real surface of the sun from the intense light and heat which it would otherwise receive.

But while recent discoveries have confirmed Sir William Herschel's theory about. the solar cloud-envelopes, they have by no means given countenance to his view that the body of the sun may possibly be cool. The darkness of the nucleus of a spot is found, on the contrary, to give proof that in that neighborhood the sun is hotter, because it parts less readily with its heat. We shall see presently how this is. Meantime let it be noticed, in passing, that a close scrutiny of large solar spots has revealed the existence of an intensely black spot in the midst of the umbra. This black spot must be regarded as the true nucleus.

The circumstance that the spots appear only on two bands of the sun's globe, corresponding to the sub-tropical zones on our own earth, led the younger Herschel to conclusions as important as those which his father had formed. He reasoned, like his father, from terrestrial analogies. On our own earth the sub-tropical zones are the regions where the great cyclonic storms have their birth, and rage with their chief fury. Here, therefore, we have the analogue of the solar spots, if only we can show reason for believing that any causes resembling those which generate the terrestrial cyclone operate upon those regions of the sun where the solar spots make their appearance.

We know that the cyclone is due to the excess of heat at the earth's equator. It is true that this excess of heat is always in operation, whereas cyclones are not perpetually raging in sub-tropical climates. Ordinarily, therefore, the excess of heat does not cause tornadoes. Certain aërial currents are generated, whose uniform motion suffices, as a rule, to adjust the conditions which the excess of heat at the equator would otherwise tend to disturb. But when through any cause the uniform action of the aërial currents is either interfered with, or is insufficient to maintain equilibrium, then cyclonic or whirling motions are generated in the disturbed atmosphere, and propagated over a wide area of the earth's surface.

Now we recognize the reason of the excess of heat at the earth's equator, in the fact that the sun shines more directly upon that part of the earth than on the zones which lie in higher latitudes. Can we find any reason for suspecting that the sun, which is not heated from without as the earth is, should exhibit a similar peculiarity? Sir John Herschel considers that we can. If the sun has an atmosphere extending to a considerable distance from his surface, then there can be little doubt that, owing to his rotation upon his axis, this atmosphere would assume the figure of an oblate spheroid, and would be deepest over the solar equator. Here, then, more of the sun's heat would be retained than at the poles, where the atmosphere is shallowest. Thus, that excess of heat at the solar equator which is necessary to complete the analogy between the sun spots and terrestrial cyclones seems satisfactorily established.

It must be remarked, however, that this reasoning, so far as the excess of heat at the sun's equator is concerned, only removes the difficulty a step. If there were indeed an increased depth of atmosphere over the sun's equator sufficing to retain the requisite excess of heat, then the amount of heat we receive from the sun's equatorial regions ought to be appreciably less than the amount emitted from the remaining portions of the solar surface. This is not found to be the case, so that either there is no such excess of absorption, or else the solar equator gives out more heat, in other words, is essentially hotter, than the rest of the sun. But this is just the peculiarity of which we want the interpretation.

It may be taken for granted, however, that there is an analogy between the sun spots and terrestrial cyclonic storms, though as yet we are not very well able to understand its nature.

Then next we come to one of the most interesting discoveries ever made respecting the sun—the discovery that the spots increase and diminish in frequency in a periodic manner. We owe this discovery to the laborious and systematic observations made by Herr Schwabe of Dessau. In these pages any account of his work would be out of place. We need only dwell upon the result, and upon other discoveries which have been made by observers who have taken up the same work.

Schwabe found, in the course of about ten and a half years, the solar spots pass through a complete cycle of changes. They become gradually more and more numerous up to a certain maximum, and then as gradually diminish. At length the sun's face becomes not only clear of spots, but a certain well-marked darkening around the border of his disk disappears altogether for a brief season. At this time the sun presents a perfectly uniform disk. Then gradually the spots return, become more and more numerous, and so the cycle of changes is run through again.

The astronomers who have watched the sun from the Kew Observatory have found that the process of change by which the spots sweep in a sort of "wave of increase" over the solar disk is marked by several minor variations. As the surface of a great sea wave will be traversed by small ripples, so the gradual increase and diminution in the number of the solar spots are characterized by minor gradations of change, which are sufficiently well marked to be distinctly cognizable.

There seems every reason for believing that the periodic changes thus noticed are due to the influence of the planets upon the solar photosphere, though in what way that influence is exerted is not at present perfectly clear. Some have thought that the mere attraction of the planets tends to produce tides of some sort in the solar envelopes. Then, since the height of a tide so produced varies as the cube or third power of the distance, it has been thought that a planet when in perihelion would generate a much larger solar tide than when in aphelion. So that, as Jupiter has a period nearly equal to the sun-spot period, it has been supposed that the attractions of this planet are sufficient to account for the great spot period. Venus, Mercury, the Earth, and Saturn have, in a similar manner, been rendered accountable for the shorter and less distinctly marked periods.

Without denying that the planets may be, and probably are, the bodies to whose influence the solar-spot periods are to be ascribed, I yet venture to express very strong doubts whether the attraction of Jupiter is so much greater in perihelion than in aphelion as to account for the fact that whereas at one season the face of the sun shows many spots, at another it is wholly free from them.[1]

However, we are not at present concerned so much with the explanation of facts as with the facts themselves. We have to consider rather what

---

[1] Recently Professor Kirkwood has published a most interesting series of inquiries, going far to prove that the real secret of the planetary influences lies in the fact that the sun's surface is not uniform, and that on a certain solar longitude the planetary influences are more effective than elsewhere.

the sun is and what he does for the solar system, than why these things are so.

Let us note, before passing to other circumstances of interest connected with the sun, that the variable condition of his photosphere must cause him to change in brilliancy as seen from vast distances. If Herr Schwabe, for instance, instead of observing the sun's spots from his watch-tower at Dessau, could have removed himself to a distance so enormous that the sun's disk would have been reduced, even in the most powerful telescope, to a mere point of light, there can be no doubt that the only effect which he would have been able to perceive would have been a gradual increase and diminution of brightness, having a period of about ten and a half years.

Our sun, therefore, viewed from the neighborhood of any of the stars, whence undoubtedly he would simply appear as one among many fixed stars, would be a "variable," having a period of ten and a half years. And further, if an observer, viewing the sun from so enormous a distance, had the means of very accurately measuring its light, he would undoubtedly discover that, while the chief variation of the sun takes place in a period of ten and a half years, its light is subjected to minor variations having shorter periods.

The discovery that the periodic changes of the sun's appearance are associated with the periodic changes in the character of the earth's magnetism is the next that we have to consider.

It had long been noticed that, during the course

of a single day, the magnetic needle exhibits a minute change of direction, taking place in an oscillatory manner. And, when the character of this vibration came to be carefully examined, it was found to correspond to a sort of effort on the needle's part to turn toward the sun. For example, when the sun is on the magnetic meridian, the needle has its mean position. This happens twice in a day, once when the sun is above the horizon and once when he is below it. Again, when the sun is midway between these two positions—which also happens twice in the day—the needle has its mean position, because the northern and the southern ends make equal efforts (so to speak) to direct themselves toward the sun. Four times in the day, then, the needle has its mean position, or is directed toward the magnetic meridian. But, when the sun is not in one of the four positions considered, that end of the needle which is nearest to him is slightly turned away from its mean position toward him. The change of position is very minute, and only the exact modes of observation made use of in the present age would have sufficed to reveal it. There it is, however, and this minute and seemingly unimportant peculiarity has been found to be full of meaning.

Had science merely measured this minute variation, the work would have given striking evidence of the exact spirit in which men of our day deal with natural phenomena. But science was to do much more. The variations of this minute variation were to be inquired into; their period was to be searched for; the laws by which they were regulated and by which their period might perhaps itself be rendered variable were to be examined; and, finally, their relation to other natural laws was to be sought after. That Science should set herself to an inquiry so delicate and so difficult, in a spirit so exacting, was nothing unusual. It is thus that all the great discoveries of our day have been effected. But it is well that the reader should recognize the careful scrutiny to which natural phenomena have been subjected before the great laws we have to consider were made known. It is thought by many, who have not been at the pains to examine what Science is really doing in our day, that the wonders she presents to men's contemplation, the startling revelations which are being made from day to day, are merely dreams and fancies, which replace indeed the dreams and fancies of old times, but have no worthier claims on our belief. Those who carefully examine the history of science will be forced to adopt a very different opinion.

The minute vibrations of the magnetic needle, thus carefully watched—day after day, month after month, year after year—were found to exhibit a yet more minute oscillatory change. They waxed and waned within narrow limits of variation, but yet in a manner there was no mistaking. The period of this oscillatory change was not to be determined, however, by the observations of a few years.[1] Between

---

[1] The reader must not understand that the account here given presents in any sense even a general view of the labors of those who have studied the earth's magnetism. I touch only on those points by which

the time when the diurnal vibration was least until it had reached its greatest extent, and thence returned to its first value, no less than ten and a half years elapsed, and a much longer time passed before the periodic character of the change was satisfactorily determined.

The reader will at once see what these observations tend to. The sun spots vary in frequency within a period of ten and a half years, and the magnetic diurnal vibrations vary within a period of the same duration. It might seem fanciful to associate the two periodic series of changes together, and doubtless when the idea first occurred to Lamont, it was not with any great expectation of finding it confirmed that he examined the evidence bearing on the point. Judging from known facts, we may see reasons for such an expectation in the correspondence of the needle's diurnal vibration with the sun's apparent motion, and the law which has been found to associate the annual variations of the magnet's power with the sun's distance. But undoubtedly when the idea occurred to Lamont it was an exceedingly bold one, and the ridicule with which the first announcement of the supposed law was received, even in scientific circles, suffices to show how unexpected that relation was which is now so thoroughly established. For a careful comparison between the two

the association between the earth's magnetism and the physical condition of the sun is most clearly indicated; because these points alone bear on the subject of this chapter. How they do so will appear further on.

periods has demonstrated that they agree most perfectly, not merely in length, but maximum for maximum, and minimum for minimum. When the sun spots are most numerous, then the daily vibration of the magnet is most extensive, while, when the sun's face is clear of spots, the needle vibrates over its smallest diurnal arc.

Then the intensity of the magnetic action has been found to depend upon solar influences. The vibrations by which the needle indicates the progress of those strange disturbances of the terrestrial magnetism which are known as magnetic storms have been found not merely to be most frequent when the sun's face is most spotted, but to occur simultaneously with the appearance of signs of disturbance in the solar photosphere. For instance, during the autumn of 1859, the eminent solar observer, Carrington, noticed the apparition of a bright spot upon the sun's surface. The light of this spot was so intense that he imagined the dark glass which protected his eye had been broken. By a fortunate coincidence, another observer, Mr. Hodgson, happened to be watching the sun at the same instant, and witnessed the same remarkable appearance. Now it was found that the self-registering magnetic instruments of the Kew Observatory had been sharply disturbed at the instant when the bright spot was seen. And afterward it was learned that the phenomena which indicate the progress of a magnetic storm had been observed in many places. Telegraphic communication was interrupted, and, in some cases, telegraphic offices were set on fire; auroras appeared both in the northern and southern hemisphere during the night which followed; and the whole frame of the earth seemed to thrill responsively to the disturbance which had affected the great central luminary of the solar system.

The reader will now see why I have discussed relations which hitherto he may perhaps have thought very little connected with my subject. He sees that there is a bond of sympathy between our earth and the sun; that no disturbance can affect the solar photosphere without affecting our earth to a greater or less degree. But if our earth, then also the other planets. Mercury and Venus, so much nearer the sun than we are, surely respond even more swiftly and more distinctly to the solar magnetic influences. But beyond our earth, and beyond the orbit of moonless Mars, the magnetic impulses speed with the velocity of light. The vast globe of Jupiter is thrilled from pole to pole as the magnetic wave rolls in upon it; then Saturn feels the shock, and then the vast distances beyond which lie Uranus and Neptune are swept by the ever-lessening yet ever-widening disturbance wave. Who shall say what outer planets it then seeks? or who, looking back upon the course over which it has travelled, shall say that planets alone have felt its effects? Meteoric and cometic systems have been visited by the great magnetic wave, and upon the dispersed members of the one and the subtle structure of the other effects even more important may have been produced than those striking phenomena which characterize the progress of the terrestrial or planetary magnetic storms.

When we remember that what is true of a relatively great solar disturbance, such as the one witnessed by Messrs. Carrington and Hodgson, is true also (however different in degree) of the magnetic influences which the sun is at every instant exerting, we see that a new and most important bond of union exists between the members of the solar family. The sun not only sways them by the vast attraction of his gravity, not only illumines them, not only warms them, but he pours forth on all his subtle yet powerful magnetic influences. A new analogy between the members of the solar system is thus introduced to reinforce those other analogies which have been held so strikingly to indicate that the ends for which our earth has been created are not different from those which the Creator had in view when He planned the other members of the solar system.[1]

And now we pass on to other discoveries, bearing at once and with equal force upon the relations between the various members of the solar scheme and

---

[1] I must remark here, once for all, that in speaking of the plans of the Creator, of His mode of working, or of the laws which He has established, I by no means intend such words to be taken literally. For want of better, such words as these must be employed in speaking of the relations between Almighty God and His universe. But in truth these relations are as inconceivable by us as infinity of space or infinity of time. We know that they exist, as certainly as we know that space and time are both infinite, but human language can no more indicate their nature than it can present to the mind an adequate picture of space or time.

upon the position which that scheme occupies in the universe.

Hitherto we have been considering the teachings of the telescope; we have now to consider what we have learned by means of an instrument of yet higher powers. As I shall have to refer very frequently, throughout this volume, to the teachings of the spectroscope, it will be well that I should briefly describe what it is that this instrument really effects. Were I simply to state the results of its use, without describing its real character, many of my readers would be disposed to believe that astronomers are as credulous as in reality they are exacting and scrupulous, where new facts and observations are in question.

The real end and aim of the telescope, as applied by the astronomer to the examination of the celestial objects, is to gather together the light which streams from each luminous point throughout space. We may regard the space which surrounds us on every side as an ocean without bounds or limits, an ocean across which there are ever sweeping waves of light, either emitted directly from the various bodies subsisting throughout space, or else reflected from their surfaces. Other forms of wave also speed across those limitless depths in all directions, but the light-waves are those which at present concern us. Our earth is as a minute island placed within the ocean of space, and to the shores of this tiny isle the light-waves bear their message from the orbs which lie like other isles amid the fathomless depths around us. With the telescope the astronomer gathers together portions of light-waves which else would have travelled in diverging directions. By thus intensifying their action, he enables the eye to become cognizant of their true nature. Precisely as the narrow channels around our shores cause the ꞏ ꞏal wave, which sweeps across the open ocean in almost insensible undulations, to rise and fall through a wide range of variation, so the telescope renders sensible the existence of light-waves which would escape the notice of the unaided eye.

The telescope, then, is essentially *a light-gatherer*.

The spectroscope is used for another purpose. It might be called the *light-sifter*. It is applied by the astronomer to analyze the light which comes to him from beyond the ocean of space, and so to enable him to learn the character of the orbs from which that light proceeds.

The principle of the instrument is simple, though the appliances by which its full powers can alone be educed are somewhat complicated.

A ray of sunlight falling on a prism of glass or crystal does not emerge unchanged in character. Different portions of the ray are differently bent, so that when they emerge from the prism they no longer travel side by side as before. The violet part of the light is bent most, the red least; the various colors from violet through blue, green, and yellow, to red being bent gradually less and less.

The prism then *sorts*, or *sifts*, the light-waves.

But we want the means of sifting the light-waves more thoroughly. The reader must bear with me

while I describe, as exactly as possible in the brief
space available to me, the way in which the first
rough work of the prism has been modified into the
delicate and significant work of the spectroscope. It
is well wo.th while to form clear views on this point,
because so many of the wonders of modern science
are associated with spectroscopic analysis.

If, through a small round hole in a shutter, light
is admitted into a darkened room, and a prism be
placed with its refracting angle downward and horizontal, a vertical spectrum, having its violet end up-
permost, will be formed on a screen suitably placed
to receive it.

But now let us consider what this spectrum really
is. If we take the light-waves corresponding to any
particular color, we know, from optical considerations, that these waves emerge from the prism in a
pencil exactly resembling in shape the pencil of white
light which falls on the prism. They therefore form
a small circular or oval image on their own proper
part of the spectrum. Hence the spectrum is in reality formed of a multitude of overlapping images,
varying in color from violet to red. It thus appears
as a rainbow-tinted streak, presenting every gradation
of color between the utmost limits of visibility at the
violet and red extremities.

If we had a square aperture to admit the light,
we should get a similar result. If the aperture were
oblong, there would still be overlapping images; but
if the length of the oblong were horizontal, then,
since each image would also be a horizontally placed

oblong, the overlapping would be less than when the images were square. Suppose we diminish the overlapping as much as possible? in other words, suppose we make the oblong slit as narrow as possible? Then, unless there were in reality an infinite number of images distributed all along the spectrum from top to bottom, the images might be so narrowed as not to overlap; in which case, of course, there would be horizontal dark spaces or gaps in our spectrum. Or, again, if we failed in finding gaps of this sort by simply narrowing the aperture, we might lengthen the spectrum by increasing the refracting angle of the prism, or by using several prisms, and so on.

The first great discovery in solar physics, by means of the analysis of the prism (though the discovery had little meaning at the time), consisted in the recognition of the fact that, by means of such devices as the above, dark gaps or cross-lines *can* be seen in the solar spectrum. In other words, light-waves of the various gradations corresponding to all the tints of the spectrum from violet to red do *not* travel to us from the great central luminary of our system. Remembering that the effect we call color is due to the length of the light-waves, the effect of red corresponding to light-waves of the greatest length, while the effect of violet corresponds to the shortest light-waves, we see that in effect the sun sends forth to the worlds which circle around him light-waves of many different lengths, but not of all. Of so complex and interesting a nature is ordinary daylight.

But spectroscopists sought to interpret these dark lines in the solar spectrum, and it was in carrying out this inquiry—which even to themselves seemed almost hopeless, and to many would appear an utter waste of time—that they lighted upon the noblest method of research yet revealed to man.

They examined the spectra of the light from incandescent substances (white-hot metals and the like), and found that in these spectra there are no dark lines.

They examined the spectra of the light from the stars, and found that these spectra are crossed by dark lines resembling those in the solar spectrum, but differently arranged.

They tried the spectra of glowing vapors, and they obtained a perplexing result. Instead of a number of dark lines across a rainbow-tinted streak, they found bright lines of various color. Some gases would give a few such lines, others many, some only one or two.

Then they tried the spectrum of the electric spark, and they found here also a series of bright lines, but not always the same series. The spectrum varied according to the substances between which the spark was taken, and the medium through which it passed.

Lastly, they found that the light from an incandescent solid or liquid, when shining through various vapors, no longer gives a spectrum without dark lines, but that the dark lines which then appear vary in position, according to the nature of the vapor through which the light has passed.

Here were a number of strange facts, seemingly too discordant and too perplexing to admit of being interpreted. Yet one discovery only was wanting to bring them all into unison.

In 1859, Kirchhoff, while engaged in observing the solar spectrum, lighted on the discovery that a certain double dark line, which had already been found to correspond exactly in position with the double bright line forming the spectrum of the glowing vapor of sodium, was intensified when the light of the sun was allowed to pass through that vapor. This at once suggested the idea that the presence of this dark line (or, rather, pair of dark lines) in the spectrum of the sun is due to the existence of the vapor of sodium in the solar atmosphere, and that this vapor has the power of absorbing the same order of light-waves as it emits. It would of course follow from this that the other dark lines in the solar spectrum are due to the presence of other absorbent vapors in its atmosphere, and that the identity of these would admit of being established in the same way, supposing this general law to hold, that a vapor emits the same light-waves that it is capable of absorbing.

Kirchhoff was soon able to confirm his views by a variety of experiments. The general principles to which his researches led—in other words, the principles which form the basis of spectrum analysis—are as follows:

1. An incandescent solid or liquid gives a continuous spectrum.

2. A glowing vapor gives a spectrum of white lines, each vapor having its own set of bright lines, so that, from the appearance of a bright-line spectrum, one can tell the nature of the vapor or vapors whose light forms the spectrum.

3. An incandescent solid or liquid shining through absorbent vapors gives a rainbow-tinted spectrum crossed by dark lines, these dark lines having the same position as the bright lines belonging to the spectra of the vapors; so that, from the arrangement of the dark lines in such a spectrum, one can tell the nature of the vapor or vapors which surround the source of light.[1]

The application of the new method of research

---

[1] To these may be added the following laws:

4. Light reflected from any opaque body gives the same spectrum as it would have given before reflection.

5. But if the opaque body be surrounded by vapors, the dark lines corresponding to these vapors make their appearance in the spectrum with a distinctness proportioned to the extent to which the light has penetrated those vapors before being reflected to us.

6. If the reflecting body be itself luminous, the spectrum belonging to it is superadded to the spectrum belonging to the reflected light.

7. Glowing vapors surrounding an incandescent source of light may cause bright lines or dark lines to appear in the spectrum, according as they are more or less heated; or, they may emit just so much light as to make up for what they absorb, in which case there will remain no trace of their presence.

8. The electric spark presents a bright-line spectrum, compounded of the spectra belonging to the vapors of those substances between which, and of those through which, the discharge takes place. According to the nature of these vapors and of the discharge itself, the relative intensity of the component parts of the spectrum will be variable.

Lastly, the appearance of the spectrum belonging to any element will vary according to the circumstances of pressure and temperature under which the element may emit light.

to the study of the solar spectrum quickly led to a
number of most interesting discoveries. It was found
that, besides sodium, the sun's atmosphere contains
the vapors of iron, calcium, magnesium, chromium,
and other metals. The dark lines corresponding to
these elements appear unmistakably in the solar
spectrum. There are other metals, such as copper
and zinc, which seem to exist in the sun, though
some of the corresponding dark lines have not yet
been recognized. As yet it has not been proved that
gold, silver, mercury, tin, lead, arsenic, antimony, or
aluminium exist in the sun—though we can by no
means conclude, nor indeed is it at all probable, that
they are absent from his substance. The dark lines
belonging to hydrogen are very well marked indeed
in solar spectrum, and, as we shall see presently, the
study of these lines has afforded most interesting information respecting the physical constitution of the sun.

Now we notice at once how importantly these researches into the sun's structure bear upon the subject of this treatise. It would be indeed interesting
to consider the actual condition of the central orb of
the planetary scheme, to picture in imagination the
metallic oceans which exist upon his surface, the
continual evaporation from those oceans, the formation of metallic clouds, and the downpour of metallic
showers upon the surface of the sun. But apart
from such considerations, and viewing Kirchhoff's
discoveries simply in their relation to the subject
of other worlds, we have enough to occupy our
attention.

If it could have been shown that, in all probability, the substance of the sun consists of materials wholly different from those which exist in this earth, the conclusion obviously to be drawn from such a discovery would be that the other planets also are differently constituted. We could not find any just reason for believing that in Jupiter or Mars there exist the elements with which we are acquainted, when we found that even the central orb of the planetary system exhibits no such feature of resemblance to the earth. But now that we know, quite certainly, that the familiar elements, iron, sodium, and calcium, exist in the sun's substance, while we are led to believe, with almost perfect assurance, that all the elements we are acquainted with also exist there, we see at once that, in all probability, the other planets are constituted in the same way. There may of course be special differences: in one planet the proportionate distribution of the elements may differ, and even differ very markedly, from that which prevails in some other planet. But the general conclusion remains, that the planets are formed of the elements which have so long been known as terrestrial; for we cannot recognize any reason for believing that our earth alone, of all the orbs which circle around the sun, resembles that great central orb in general constitution.[1]

---

[1] It will be seen, in the chapter on Meteors and Comets, that this conclusion has a most important bearing on the views we are to form respecting the original formation of the planetary scheme.

Now, we have in this general law a means of passing beyond the bounds of the solar system, and forming no indistinct conceptions as to the existence and character of worlds circling around other suns. For it will be seen, in the chapter on the stars, that these orbs, like our sun, contain in their substance many of the so-called terrestrial elements, while it may not unsafely be asserted that all, or nearly all, those elements, and few or no elements unknown to us, exist in the substance of every single star that shines upon us from the celestial concave. Hence we conclude that around those suns also there circle orbs constituted like themselves, and therefore containing the elements with which we are familiar. And the mind is immediately led to speculate on the uses which those elements are intended to subserve. If iron, for example, is present in some noble orb circling around Sirius, we speculate not unreasonably respecting the existence on that orb—either now or in the past, or at some future time—of beings capable of applying that metal to the useful purposes which man makes it subserve. The imagination suggests immediately the existence of arts and sciences, trades and manufactures, on that distant world. We know how intimately the use of iron has been associated with the progress of human civilization, and though we must ever remain in ignorance of the actual condition of intelligent beings in other worlds, we are yet led, by the mere presence of an element which is so closely related to the wants of man, to believe, with a new confidence, that for such beings those worlds must in truth have been fashioned.

I would fain dwell longer on the thoughts suggested by the researches of Kirchhoff. Gladly too would I enter at length on an account of those interesting discoveries which have been made in connection with the last two total eclipses of the sun. The requirements of space, however, and some doubt as to the direct bearing of the last-named discoveries on the subject I have in hand, warn me to forbear. One point, however, remains, which is too intimately connected with my subject to be passed over.

I refer to the sun's corona.

It has been proved that the solar prominences consist of glowing vapors, hydrogen being their chief constituent. It has been found also, by comparing Mr. Lockyer's observations of the prominence-spectra with Dr. Frankland's elaborate researches into the peculiarities presented by the spectrum of hydrogen at different pressures, that even in the very neighborhood of the solar photosphere these vapors probably exist at a pressure so moderate as to indicate that the limits of the sun's vaporous envelope cannot lie very far (relatively) from the outer solar cloud-layer.

Now, the solar corona has been seen, during total eclipses of the sun, to extend to a distance at least equal to the sun's diameter from the eclipsed orb. So that, assuming the corona to be a solar atmosphere, it would have a depth of about eight hundred and fifty thousand miles, and being also drawn toward the sun by his enormous attractive energy (exceeding more than twenty-seven times that of the earth), it could not fail to exert a pressure on his surface exceeding many thousand-fold that of our air upon the earth. In fact, such an atmosphere, let its outermost layers be as rare as we can conceive, would yet have its lower layers absolutely liquefied, if not solidified, by the enormous pressure to which they would be subjected. We cannot, then, believe this corona to be a solar atmosphere.

Yet it is quite impossible to dissociate the corona, either wholly or in part, from the sun. I am aware that physicists of eminence have attempted to do this, and not only so, but to make of the zodiacal light a terrestrial phenomenon. But they have overlooked considerations which oppose themselves irresistibly to such a conclusion.

In the first place, the mere fact that, during a total eclipse, the moon looks black, in the very heart of the corona, affords, when properly understood, the most conclusive evidence that the light of the corona comes from behind the moon. If the glare of our atmosphere could by any possibility account for the corona (which is not the case), then that glare should appear over the moon's disk also. That this is so is proved by the fact that, when the glare really does cover the moon, as while the sun is but slightly eclipsed, the moon is not projected as a black disk on the background of the *sky*, though, where her outline crosses the sun, it appears black, by contrast with the intensity of his light.[1] The point seems, however, too obvious to need discussion.

And, secondly, as Mr. Baxendell has pointed out, during totality the part of the earth's atmosphere between the eye and the corona is not illuminated by the sun. Over a wide space all round the sun we are looking through an atmosphere which is completely dark. In fact, if the earth's atmosphere alone were in question, we ought to see a dark or negative corona around the sun, the illuminated atmosphere only beginning to be faintly visible at a considerable angular distance from the sun. This argument, rightly understood, is altogether decisive of the question.[2]

---

[1] It is also shown most conclusively, by a photograph of the eclipse of August, 1868, taken an instant before the totality. Here we see the glare trenching upon the moon's disk (elsewhere black), as it should theoretically. So soon as totality commenced, the glare had reached the moon's limb, whence it must immediately have passed quickly away.

[2] In fact, if we take the mode of reasoning by which Mr. Lockyer has endeavored to get over certain physical difficulties presently to be mentioned, we shall be able to point definitely to the place where his argument fails. He says, conceive a tiny moon placed so as to appear coincident with the centre of the sun's disk. There will be atmospheric glare as well as direct sunlight. Now, conceive this small moon to expand until it all but covers the sun. Still there will be glare and a certain small proportion of direct sunlight. So far his reasoning is most just. But when he allows his expanding moon to cover the sun, and to extend beyond the solar disk as in total eclipse, the atmospheric glare can no longer be assumed to exist all round the expanding moon: at the moment when the moon just hides the sun, the glare begins to leave the moon, a gradually expanding black ring being formed round that body. It is only necessary to consider where the glare comes from to see that this must be so.

I have taken no account of diffraction here, because it has been

But the spectroscope has given certain very perplexing evidence respecting the light of the corona, and it remains that we should endeavor to see how that evidence bears on the interesting problem which the corona presents to our consideration.

During the total eclipse of last August the American observers found that the spectrum of the corona is continuous, but crossed by certain bright lines. If we accept the absence of dark lines as established by the evidence (which is doubtful), this result seems at first sight very difficult to explain. Referring to the principles of spectroscopic analysis stated on pp. 57, 58, it will be seen that we should be led to infer that the corona consists of incandescent matter surrounded by certain glowing gases. It is difficult to suppose that this is the real explanation of the phenomenon.

Mr. Lockyer suggests that, if the corona shone by reflecting the solar light, the continuous spectrum might be accounted for by supposing the light from the glowing vapors around the sun to supply the part wanting where the solar dark lines are, and that some of these vapors shining yet more brightly would exhibit their bright lines upon the continuous background of the spectrum. This view, as applied by Mr. Lockyer to the theory that the corona is a terrestrial phenomenon, is untenable, for the reasons already adduced. But, independently of those rea-

bundantly proved that no corona of appreciable width could be formed around the moon during total eclipse by the diffraction of the rays of light as they pass near the moon's limb.

sons, there are others which render such a solution of the difficulty unavailable.

Now, remembering that we have two established facts for our guidance—(1) the fact that the corona cannot be a solar atmosphere, and (2) the fact that it must be a solar appendage—I think a way may be found toward a satisfactory explanation.

Let it be premised that the bright lines of the coronal spectrum correspond in position to those seen in the spectrum of the aurora, and that the same lines are seen in the spectrum of the zodiacal light, and in that of the phosphorescent light occasionally seen over the heavens at night.

Since we have every reason to believe that the light of the aurora is due to electrical discharges taking place in the upper regions of the air, we are invited to the belief that the coronal light may be due to similar discharges taking place between the particles (of whatever nature) constituting the corona.

Now, though the appearance of an aurora is due to some special terrestrial action (however excited), yet the material substances between which the discharges take place must be assumed to be at all times present in the upper regions of air. In all probability, they are the particles of those meteors which the earth is continually encountering. And since we know that meteor-systems must be aggregated in far greater numbers near the sun than near the earth, we may regard the coronal light as due to electrical discharges excited by the sun's action, and taking place between the members of such systems. Besides this light, however, there must necessarily be a large proportion of light reflected from these meteoric bodies. In this way the peculiar character of the coronal spectrum may be readily accounted for. We know, from the auroral spectrum, that the principal bright lines due to the electrical discharges would be precisely where we see bright lines in the coronal spectrum. But, besides these, there would be fainter bright lines corresponding to the various elements which exist in the meteoric masses. These elements, we know, are the same as those in the substance of the sun. Thus the bright lines would correspond in position with the dark lines of the solar spectrum. Hence, as light reflected by the meteors would give the ordinary solar spectrum, there would result from the combination a continuous spectrum, on which the bright lines first mentioned would be seen, as during the American eclipse.

What the polariscope has told us respecting the corona is in accordance with this view.

In the same way the quality of the zodiacal light admits of being perfectly accounted for, without resorting to the hypothesis that this phenomenon is a terrestrial one.[1]

---

[1] It was with some surprise that, at a late meeting of the Royal Astronomical Society, I heard Dr. Balfour Stewart put forward, even as a hypothesis, so startling a proposition as this. That the region of the counter trades may be at times illuminated by electrical discharges will serve to account very well for the occasional phosphorescent appearance of the whole heavens at night—but the portion of the heavens illuminated by the zodiacal light has no relation whatever to the atmospheric region in which the counter trades prevail. The hypothesis, indeed, is wholly untenable.

The explanation thus put forward has at least the advantage of being founded on well-established relations. We know that the auroral light is associated with the earth's magnetism, and that meteoric bodies are continually falling upon the earth's atmosphere. We know, also, that the sun exerts magnetic influences a thousand-fold more intense than those of the earth, and that in his neighborhood there must be many million times more meteoric systems.

But we have other and independent reasons, which must not be overlooked, for considering the corona to be of some such nature as I have suggested. Leverrier has shown that there probably exists in the neighborhood of the sun a family of bodies whose united mass suffices appreciably to affect the motions of the planet Mercury. It would not be safe to neglect considerations thus vouched for.

Mr. Baxendell also, has shown that certain periodic variations in the earth's magnetism point to the existence of such a family of bodies; and he has been able to assign to them a position according well with that determined by Leverrier.

Now, whatever opinion we form as to the exact character of the system of bodies pointed to by the researches of Leverrier and Baxendell—whether we suppose that system to form a zone around the sun,[1]

---

[1] I am not here referring to Humboldt's notion that the zodiacal light is due to a zone of small bodies round the sun; a view which only derives importance from the fact that Sir John Herschel has been at the pains to contradict it. It need hardly be said that Sir John Herschel's opinion has a weight which is altogether wanting to Humboldt's, so far as astronomical matters are concerned.

or that (as I believe) the system is merely due to the aggregation of meteoric perihelia in the sun's neighborhood—we may be quite certain of this, that during a total solar eclipse the system could not fail to become visible. Hence there is a double objection to the view put forward by Mr. Lockyer and others. In the first place, it fails to account for the appearance presented by the corona; in the second place, it fails to render an account of the implied non-appearance of the system which, according to the researches of Leverrier and Baxendell, circles around the sun.

It will be seen, in the chapter on "Meteors and Comets," how important a bearing these views respecting the nature of the corona have upon the history of the solar system. It has been partly for this reason that I have here briefly considered the matter; but there is another and a most important relation in which these views must be regarded.

We know that the sun is the sole source whence light and heat are plentifully supplied to the worlds which circle around him. The question immediately suggests itself—Whence does the sun derive those amazing stores of force from whence he is continually supplying his dependent worlds? We know that, were the sun a mass of burning matter, he would be consumed in a few thousand years. We know that, were he simply a heated body, radiating light and heat continually into space, he would in like manner have exhausted all his energies in a few thousand years—a mere day in the history of his system.

Whence, then, comes the enormous supply of force which he has afforded for millions on millions of years, and which also our reason tells us he will continue to afford while the worlds which circle around him have need of it—in other words, for countless ages yet to come?

Now, there are two ways in which the solar energies might be maintained. The mere contraction of the solar substance, Helmholtz tells us, would suffice to supply such enormous quantities of heat that, if the heat actually given out by the sun were due to this cause alone, there would not, in many thousands of years, be any perceptible diminution of the sun's diameter. But, secondly, the continual downfall of meteors upon the sun would cause an emission of heat in quantities vast enough for the wants of all the worlds circling round him; while his increase of mass from this cause would not be rendered perceptible in thousands of years, either by any change in his apparent size or by changes in the motions of his family of worlds.[1]

It seems far from unlikely that both these processes are in operation at the same time. Certainly the latter is, for we know, from the motions of the

---

[1] Altogether undue stress has been laid upon the probable change in the length of the year, owing to the downfall of meteors upon the sun's mass. It is forgotten that the crowded meteors forming the solar corona are *already* within the earth's orbit, and therefore already produce their full effect on the length of the year. The subsidence of all these bodies at once upon the sun would not affect the length of the year, though it would lead to certain modifications in the secular perturbations of the earth's orbit in figure and position.

meteoric bodies which reach the earth, that myriads of these bodies must continually fall upon the sun. And if the corona and zodiacal light really be due to the existence of flights of meteoric systems circling around the sun, or to the existence in his neighborhood of the perihelia of many meteoric systems, then there must be a supply of light and heat from this source, very nearly if not quite sufficient to account for the whole solar emission.

It is well worthy of notice, too, that the association between meteors and comets has an important bearing on this question. We know that the most remarkable characteristic of comets is the enormous diffusion of their substance. Now, in this diffusion there resides an enormous fund of force. The contraction of a large comet to dimensions corresponding to a very moderate mean density would be accompanied by the emission of a vast supply of heat. And the question is worth inquiring into, whether we can indeed assume that the meteors which reach our atmosphere are solid bodies, and not rather of cometic diffusion; since it is difficult otherwise to account for the light and heat which they emit. Friction through the rarer upper strata of our atmosphere will certainly not account for these phenomena; nor, I think, will the compression of the atmosphere in front of the meteors; on the other hand, the sudden contraction of a diffused vapor would be accompanied by precisely such results. But, be this as it may, it is certain that a large portion of the substance of every comet is in a singularly diffused

state. And since the meteoric systems circling in
countless millions round the sun are, in all probability, associated in the most intimate manner with
comets, we may recognize in this diffusion, as well
as in the mere downfall of meteors, the source of an
enormous supply of light and heat.

And lastly, turning from our sun to the other
suns which shine in uncounted myriads throughout
space, we see the same processes at work upon them
all. Each star-sun has its coronal and its zodiacal
disks, formed by meteoric and cometic systems; for
otherwise each would quickly cease to be a sun.
Each star-sun emits, no doubt, the same magnetic influences which give to the zodiacal light and to the
solar corona their peculiar characteristics. And thus
the worlds which circle round those orbs may resemble our own in all those relations which we refer to
terrestrial magnetism, as well as in the circumstance
that on them also there must be, as on our own
earth, a continual downfall of minute meteors. In
those worlds, perchance, the magnetic compass directs
the traveller over desert wastes or trackless oceans;
in their skies, the aurora displays its brilliant stream-
ers; while, amid the constellations which deck their
heavens, meteors sweep suddenly into view, and comets extend their vast length athwart the celestial
vault, a terror to millions, but a subject of study
and research to the thoughtful.

CHAPTER III

THE INFERIOR PLANETS

IN considering the habitability of various portions of the solar system, we have to draw a marked distinction between the planets which travel within the orbit of the earth and those which lie beyond its range. So far, indeed, as our belief in these orbs being inhabited is concerned, we may apply the same processes of reasoning to one set of planets as to the other. Until it has been demonstrated that no form of life can exist upon a planet, the presumption must be that the planet is inhabited. But it is impossible to contemplate the various members of our solar system, without being led to consider their physical habitudes rather with relation to the wants of such creatures as exist upon our own earth, than merely with reference to the existence of life of some sort upon their surface. Viewing Venus and Mercury in this way, we have a different set of relations to deal with than we find among the outer planets. We are struck, at once, with the marked effects which seem associable with their comparative proximity to the sun's orb. This feature and the shortness of their period of revolution—that is, of their year—are the characteristic peculiarities we have to deal with.

I would willingly pay some attention here to the story of Vulcan, the planet which has been supposed to circle yet more closely than Mercury around the centre of our system, were it not for the great doubt in which the existence of this planet seems enshrouded. If, on the one hand, we have the evidence of Lescarbault that, on a certain day, and at a certain hour, he saw a dark object, round like a planet, crossing the face of the sun, we have also the evidence of Liais, whose name is much better known among astronomers, that at that very hour there was no such object on the solar disk. There is nothing to render the existence of an intra-Mercurial planet at all unlikely; and there are many observations which scarcely seem explicable on any other hypothesis. Still, as yet we have not that clear and unmistakable evidence which would permit me to speak of Vulcan as a planet known to astronomers, and I wish, while within the bounds of the solar system, to limit myself to the consideration of bodies which have been recognized and examined.

Mercury circles around the sun in the brief period of eighty-eight days, or rather less than three of our months. So that, if the planet has seasons, these must be severally about three weeks long. His distance from the sun varies between somewhat wide limits, owing to the eccentricity of his orbit. When he is nearest to the sun, he receives ten and a half times more light and heat from that luminary than we do; but, when he removes to his greatest distance, the light and heat he receives are reduced by more than one-half. Even then, however, the sun blazes in the skies of Mercury with a disk four and a half times larger than that which he presents to the observer on earth.

Undoubtedly these peculiarities, the shortness of the Mercurial year, and the immense amount of light and heat poured by the sun upon the planet, are circumstances which do not encourage, at first sight, the belief that any creatures can subsist upon this planet resembling those with which we are familiar. We see, at once, that all forms of vegetation in Mercury must differ in a very striking manner from those which exist upon the earth, because their structure has to be adapted to much more rapid changes of temperature. And the existence of a totally distinct flora suggests at once the belief that animal life on Mercury must be very different from what we see around us.

Let us, however, proceed a few steps further.

It has been found that Mercury rotates upon his axis, and, if we may put faith in the observations of Schröter, the Mercurial day is only a few minutes longer than our own. But, though the fact of the planet's rotation has been observed, it has not been found possible to determine in what position the axis of rotation lies. It has been said that the planet's equator is much more inclined than the earth's to the plane in which the planet travels; but little reliance can be placed on the evidence which has been adduced in favor of this view.

We are thus left altogether in doubt as to the nature of the Mercurial seasons. That the planet has seasons of some sort we are certain, because, even if the axis were so placed that perpetual spring reigned upon the planet—I mean, that the days and nights were at all times and in all places equal—yet his varying distance from the sun would give changes of temperature quite as marked as those which characterize our seasons in England, and very much more marked than those known in tropical regions. Of course, if this is the actual arrangement, there are different climates in different parts of the planet. Near his poles, the sun, though visible for half the Mercurial day, attains yet but a low elevation above the horizon; just as he does on a spring day within our own polar circles. At the equator the sun passes day after day to the zenith, and pours down upon the planet an amount of light and heat far exceeding the light and heat of our tropical climates. A sun immediately overhead, and showing a diameter varying from more than twice to more than three times that of our sun, must be a noble, and may be a terrible, phenomenon in the skies of Mercury.

There is yet another arrangement by which, to a portion of the planet, at any rate, the Mercurial seasons might be tempered. If his axis is so placed that what would be the winter season, were his orbit not eccentric, takes place, for one hemisphere, when the planet is nearest to the sun, then undoubtedly it may very well happen (the inclination of his axis being suitably adjusted) that this so-called winter season is the warmest part of the year for that hemisphere. In this case there would be the least possible violence in the succession of the Mercurial seasons for that hemisphere. But in the other hemisphere the seasonal changes would be correspondingly intensified.

In either of these cases it is readily conceivable that even forms of life resembling those we are acquainted with on earth might exist on Mercury, and that without any special provision for tempering the great heat and light of the sun. Those regions which correspond to our temperate and tropical zones would indeed scarcely be habitable; but the polar regions of the planet would not form a disagreeable abode.

If, however, the equator of the planet is very much inclined to the plane in which Mercury travels, it cannot be doubted that no form of life known upon earth can possibly exist upon Mercury, *without* some special arrangements for tempering the seasonal changes. This will appear when we come to deal with the effect of the great inclination which some astronomers have ascribed to the equator of Venus, and therefore we need not consider the relation with regard to Mercury, of whose axial inclination no trustworthy information has hitherto been obtained.

It remains for us to consider what sort of provision may have been made to temper the great heat poured by the sun upon Mercury.

The climate of a planet, considered generally, is

largely influenced by the nature of the planet's atmosphere. We have very clear evidence on this point,
in the effects which we notice on our own earth. If
we ascend to the summit of a lofty mountain, we
find the air much colder than at its base. In India,
though the full heat of a tropical sun is poured day
after day upon the snowy summits of the Himalayas,
yet the air continues colder than in the bitterest midwinter weather experienced by us in England. Not
that the solar rays have no power. The heat is, in
reality, even greater than on the plains, because it
has not been intercepted by vapor-laden air. But
the air itself is not heated. Owing to its extreme
rarity and dryness, it neither impedes the passage
of the sun's heat to the earth, nor prevents the return of that heat from the earth by radiation or
reflection; and this very fact, that it does not impede
the passage of heat, means nothing else than that the
air does not become heated.[1]

We have, then, so far as a rare atmosphere is concerned, two points to dwell upon—the readiness with

---

[1] The following passage, quoted by Professor Tyndall from Hooker's
"Himalayan Journals," illustrates the peculiarities referred to above:
"At 10,000 feet, in December, at 9 A.M., I saw the mercury mount
to 132°, while the temperature of shaded snow hardly was 22°. At
13,100 feet, in January, at 9 A.M., it has stood at 98°, with a difference of 68.2°, and at 10 A.M at 114°, with a difference of 81.4°, while
the radiating thermometer on the snow had fallen at sunrise to 0.7°."
Such observations as these are well worth studying. It is interesting
to consider that at the summit of the highest peaks of the Himalayas
the midday heat of the sun must sometimes be near, if not above, the
boiling point corresponding to those places, since water would boil on
Mount Everest at a temperature of little more than 160°.

which such an atmosphere permits the sun's heat to reach the surface of a planet, and the readiness with which it permits the planet's heat to pass away into space. Now, we might feel doubtful which of these two effects was chiefly to be regarded, were it not that on our own earth we have experience of the effects of a very rare atmosphere. We know that the climate of very elevated regions is relatively much cooler than that of places on the plain. Thus we learn that the direct heating powers of the sun are not so much to be considered, in judging of the climate of any region, as the quality of the atmosphere.

Yet we must not deceive ourselves by inferring that mere rarity of atmosphere can compensate fully for an increased intensity of solar heat. It is not true that the climate of a place on the slopes of the Andes or the Himalayas corresponds to that of a region on the plain which has an atmosphere equally warm. The circumstances are, in fact, wholly different. On the plain there is, it is true, the same amount of heat in the case supposed: but the air is denser and more moisture-laden; the nights are warmer because the skies are less clear and the heat escaping from the earth is intercepted by clouds or by the transparent aqueous vapor in the air; and, lastly, there is not so great a contrast between the warmth of the air and the direct heat of the solar rays.

If the atmosphere of Mercury, therefore, be excessively rare, as some have supposed, so as to afford

an Alpine or Himalayan climate in comparison with
the tremendous heat we should otherwise ascribe to
the climate of the planet, there would by no means
result a state of things resembling that with which
we are familiar on earth. We must not, in our
anxiety to people Mercury with creatures such as we
know of, blind ourselves to the difficulties which have
to be encountered. We cannot thin the Mercurial air,
without adding to the direct effects of the sun upon
the Mercurial inhabitants. Whether in this way we
increase the habitability of the planet may be doubted
when we consider that the direct action of the sun's
rays upon the tropical regions of Mercury, thus de-
prived of atmospheric protection, would produce a
heat four or five times greater than that of boiling
water. It will hardly be thought that the intense
cold in the shade, or during the Mercurial night,
would compensate for so terrible a heat. In fact,
this view of the Mercurial climate would lead us to
find a close resemblance between the inhabitants of
the planet and the unfortunates described by Dante
as doomed

"A sofferir tormenti e caldi e gieli."

It would seem hard to believe in the existence of
any organized forms under such conditions, unless
perhaps such "microscopic creatures, with siliceous
coverings," as Whewell proposed to people Venus
with.

However, we have yet to consider whether an
atmosphere of a different sort might not be better

suited to the requirements of Mercury. We have seen the effects of a rare atmosphere, let us inquire into those which might be ascribed to a dense one.

The ordinary effect of a dense atmosphere we know to be an increase of heat, which is certainly not what we require in the case of Mercury. Nor are we familiar with any region upon our earth in which a dense atmosphere produces a contrary *climatic* effect; so that we have no analogy to support us in the belief that, possibly, a dense atmosphere might, under particular circumstances, serve to guard a planet from the solar rays. It seems possible, however, that an atmosphere might be so constituted as to remain almost constantly loaded with heavy cloud-masses. In this case, it by no means follows that such effects would follow as we ordinarily associate with a moisture-laden atmosphere. Up to a certain point, doubtless, the increase of moisture in the air tends to an increase of warmth; because the aqueous vapor exercises a greater effect in preventing the escape of heat from the earth than in guarding the earth from the solar rays. And, as I have said, the only *climatic* effect we can associate with the frequent presence of large quantities of ·aqueous vapor in the air, or therefore with an ordinarily clouded state of the sky, is that of a general increase of heat. But, just as we know that a cloudy day is not necessarily nor even commonly a warm day, it may well be that an atmosphere so dense as to be at all times cloud-laden serves as a protection from the sun's intense heat. So that, instead of assigning dense atmospheres exclusively to the more distant planets, as some astronomers have done, we might be led to see in an envelope of great density the means of defending the inhabitants of Mercury and Venus from the otherwise unendurable rays of their near neighbor, the sun.

Although Mercury is not a planet which can be satisfactorily examined with the telescope, yet, so far as can be judged from his aspect, his atmosphere is in reality much denser than our earth's, and loaded with cloud-masses of enormous extent. Still the evidence on these points is far from satisfactory; and there is one peculiarity of the planet which does not accord with this view of the constitution of his atmosphere. Undoubtedly, if the light we receive from Mercury came from a cloudy envelope, it would be more brilliant than the light we should receive from the surface of continents and oceans. In fact, the most brilliant light we could receive from a globe of a given size, placed at a given distance from the sun, would be that which would be reflected were such a globe covered with clouds. Now, there can be no doubt whatever that Mercury does not reflect the same proportion of light from his surface that some of the planets do. He would be, when favorably situated, the brightest of all the planets were this so;[1] though, seen as he always is,

---

[1] Placing Mercury in perihelion and at his elongation, we get a half disk, the planet about 90,000,000 miles from us, and about 30,000,000 from the sun, his diameter about 3,000 miles. Now, if we wish to compare the light he then sends us with that of Jupiter at his brightest, on

on the bright background of a full twilight sky, he would not make so striking an appearance as Jupiter does when in opposition. This, however, is not the case. I remember being much struck by the superior light of Jupiter, on the afternoon of February 23, 1868, when the two planets were very close together, Mercury being nearly at his brightest, whereas Jupiter, then near conjunction, was considerably less bright than when in opposition. Venus was close by, and outshone both Mercury and Jupiter.

It seems difficult, therefore, to believe that the light of Mercury comes from a cloudy envelope. But there is still one supposition which may restore our belief in the habitability of the planet by creatures not very different from those which inhabit our earth. If it has a double cloud-envelope, the upper like our cirrus clouds, less compact than the lower, and permitting a portion of the sunlight to pass through, it is possible that the lower cloud-layer would be seen partly in shadow. I must admit that the explanation is not quite satisfactory, because,

---

the assumption of equal reflective powers, we must take Jupiter at a distance of about 360,000,000 miles from us, and about 450,000,000 miles from the sun, showing a full disk, his diameter about 90,000 miles (I put all the numbers *round*, for convenience of calculation). We find, then, that the ratio of Mercury's light to Jupiter's is

$$\frac{1}{2} \frac{(3,000)^2}{(90,000,000)^2 \times (30,000,000)^2} : \frac{(90,000)^2}{(360,000,000)^2 \times (450,000,000)^2}$$

or $\frac{1}{2} (4)^2 (15)^2 : (30)^2$, or exactly 2 to 1.

The observation above cited is sufficient to prove that a very different state of things actually prevails; in other words, that the reflective powers of the two planets are very different. Unless, indeed, Jupiter shines in part by inherent light.

just as much light as the outer clouds intercepted
they would reflect; still, it is conceivable that the
usual arrangement of these clouds may be such, that
to us, who do not look at the planet in the direction
in which the sun's rays fall, but somewhat aslant,
the shadows of the upper clouds upon the dense and
compact lower envelope may be rendered in large
part visible.

After all, the reader may prefer the view which
recognizes in the polar regions of Mercury places
suitable for organic existences, while the equatorial
and neighboring regions are zones of fire, whose dan-
gers the bravest Mercurials, the very Livingstones
upon that planet, would not dare to face. We may
picture to ourselves, on this view, the various con-
trivances by which the inhabitants of the two polar
(that is, in reality, temperate) circles manage to com-
municate.   There may be regions where favoring
circumstances narrow the uninhabitable zone so much
that the inhabitants of one polar circle may travel to
the other (or, at least, cross the most dangerous portion of the hot zone) in the course of the Mercurial
night. Or perhaps tunnels may be run, or sheltered
cuttings made, along which the voyage may be made
in comparative safety. Ocean communication there
can be none, if the Mercurial skies are clear, since
the sun's heat on the tropical zone would suffice to
boil away any water which might find its way there.

Certainly, the smallness of the planet and the
diminished effects of gravity upon its surface would
tend to make communication much easier, and the

construction of protective tunnels or cuttings a comparatively light task. What the exact force of gravity at the surface of Mercury may be we do not
know, because our means of determining the mass of
the planet are not so satisfactory as in the case
of the other primary members of the solar system.
If Mercury had a satellite we could tell his weight
at once. If he were as large as Venus we could tell
his weight by observing his effect in disturbing the
motions of that planet. As it is, the only means we
have of weighing Mercury is the observation of his
effect in disturbing any comet which may pass near
him. In this way the planet has been weighed, but
the balance thus employed is not a satisfactory one
altogether, because we are not quite certain how
much of the disturbance of a comet when near Mercury is due to the planet's attraction. Formerly it
was supposed that the mean density of Mercury was
equal to that of lead; but, from the perturbations of
Encke's comet in Mercury's neighborhood, astronomers have been led to the conclusion that the density of the planet is not more than one-sixth greater
than our earth's. It follows that, as his diameter is
little more than three thousand miles, our earth
is about fifteen times as heavy as Mercury. Gravity
at his surface is such that a pound weight of ours
would weigh rather less than seven ounces on Mercury. Hence the creatures which seem to us most
unwieldy—the elephant, the hippopotamus, and the
rhinoceros, or even those vast monsters, the mam-
moth, the mastodon, and the megatherium, which

bore sway over our globe in far-off eras—might emulate on Mercury the agility of the antelope or the greyhound.

There can be no doubt that, where gravity acts so feebly, all engineering operations would be rendered very much simpler—bridges could have a wider span and yet be stronger than our terrestrial ones, buildings could be loftier and yet be raised more easily, and transit of all sorts would be effected much more readily, while at the same time the distances to be traversed are very much less than on our earth, since the surface of Mercury is little more than one-seventh of the earth's.

The peculiarities which characterize Venus are for the most part similar in kind to those we have had to consider in the case of Mercury. But at the outset of our inquiries into the physical habitudes of this most beautiful planet, we must point to the striking resemblance which it bears, in some respects, to our own earth. So far, indeed, as telescopic and physical researches have yet led us, the planet Mars, as we shall presently see, appears to exhibit habitudes more closely corresponding to those we are apt to consider essential to the wants of living creatures. But in size, in situation, and in density, in the length of her seasons and of her rotation, in the figure of her orbit and in the amount of light and heat she receives from the sun, Venus bears a more striking resemblance to the earth than any orb within the solar system. In fact, there is no other pair of planets between which so many analogies can be traced as between Venus and the earth. Uranus and Neptune are similar in many respects, but they differ in at least as many. Jupiter and Saturn are, in a sense, the brother giants of the solar scheme, while the dwarf orbs Mars and Mercury present many striking points of similarity; but between neither of these pairs can we trace so many features of resemblance as those which characterize the twin planets Venus and Terra, while the features of dissimilarity in either pair are perhaps even more obvious than the points of resemblance. Had Venus but a moon as the earth has, we might doubt whether, in the whole universe, two orbs exist which are so strikingly similar to each other.

And here we may pause for a moment to consider one of the most perplexing enigmas that has ever been presented to astronomers. Are we indeed certain that Venus has no moon? The question seems a strange one, when it is remembered that year after year Venus has been examined by the most eminent modern observers, armed with telescopes of the most exquisite defining power, without any trace of a companion orb being noticed. Nor, indeed, can any reasonable doubts be entertained respecting the moonless condition of Venus, by those who appreciate the character of modern telescopic observations; and yet, if I had begun this paragraph by stating the evidence in favor of the existence of a satellite, I believe that nearly every reader would have come to the conclusion that most certainly the Planet of

Love has an attendant orb. They are not amateur observers only who have seen a moon attending on Venus, but such astronomers as Cassini and Short, the latter with two different telescopes and four different eye-pieces. Four times, between May 3 and 11, 1761, Montaigne saw a body near Venus, which presented a phase similar to that of the planet, precisely as a satellite would have done. From these observations M. Baudouin deduced for the new star a diameter of about two thousand miles, and a distance from Venus nearly equal to that which separates the moon from the earth. In March, 1764, again, Rödkier saw the enigmatical companion; Horrebow saw it a few days later; and Montbaron saw it in varying positions on March 15, 28, and 29. Lastly, Scheuten, who witnessed the transit of Venus in 1761, declares that he saw a satellite accompany Venus across the face of the sun. So that we cannot be greatly surprised that even so skilful an observer as the late Admiral Smyth was disposed to believe in the existence of a satellite of Venus. "The contested satellite is, perhaps," he remarked, "extremely minute, while some parts of its body may be less capable of reflecting light than others; and when the splendor of its primary and our inconvenient station for watching it are considered, it must be conceded that, however slight the hope may be, the search ought not to be relinquished."

There is little occasion to dwell upon Venus's moonless condition, because the inferior planets are much less affected by the want of a moon than a

superior planet would be. The service rendered by
our own moon, as a luminary of the night, is the
least important work she does in our behalf. It is
as the chief regulator of the tides that the moon be-
friends us most usefully. Now, Venus has no need
of lunar tides. Assuming that she has oceans such
as those which exist upon the earth, her solar tides
must be about two and a half times as high as the
solar tides raised in our own oceans. And since our
lunar tidal wave is about two and a half times as
high as the solar one, we have tides ranging between
the highest spring tides, which are three and a half
times as high as the solar tide alone, and the lowest
neap tides, which are only one and a half times as
high as the solar wave. Venus has constant tides,
therefore, corresponding very closely to the mean
tides on our own earth; and therefore perfectly well
adapted to subserve all the purposes which our tides
render us, only with less variety in their mode of
operation. Mercury also has sufficiently high solar
tides, supposing he has extensive oceans (which may
reasonably be questioned), since the smallness of
his dimensions, tending of course to diminish the
difference of action on which the sun's tidal influence
depends, is fully compensated by his great proximity
to that orb.

Venus has a year of two hundred and twenty-four
days, seventeen hours, very nearly, and her distance
from the sun, which varies little during the course
of a year, is somewhat less than three-fourths of
that which separates the sun from us. Her day is

about thirty-five minutes shorter than ours, and her globe somewhat smaller than the earth's.

It is clear that, merely in the greater proximity of Venus to the sun, there is little to render at least the larger proportion of her surface uninhabitable by such beings as exist upon our earth. The sun, as seen in her skies, has a diameter one-third larger than he presents to us; and his apparent surface-dimensions, on which, of course, his heating and illuminating powers depend, are greater in the pro-portion of about sixteen to nine. This undoubtedly would render his heat almost unbearable in the equatorial regions of Venus, but in her temperate and subarctic regions a climate which we should find well suited to our requirements might very well ex-ist; while her polar regions might correspond to our temperate zones, and be the abode of the most active and enterprising races existing upon her surface.

Here, however, we have been supposing that Venus has seasons resembling our own in character—in other words, that her axis of rotation is inclined at about the same angle to the plane in which she travels. Observations have been made, according to which a very different state of things would appear to prevail. It has been said, on the authority of observers of some eminence, that her axis is inclined only 15° to the plane of her orbit.[1] If this is really the case, a

---

[1] Why is it that, in so many works of popular astronomy, the mis-take is made of giving the inclination of a planet's equator to the orbit as the inclination of the axis to that plane? In nine out of ten astro-

number of singular and somewhat complicated relations are presented, the result of which it may be interesting to exhibit to the reader—especially as there is very little doubt that in the case of Uranus an axial peculiarity of this sort actually exists.[1]

In the first place, the arctic regions of Venus extend within fifteen degrees of her equator (if the axis is really bowed as supposed), while the tropics extend within fifteen degrees of her poles—so that two zones, larger by far than the temperate zones of our earth, belong both to her arctic and to her tropical regions. It is difficult to say whether her equatorial, her polar, or her arctico-tropical regions would be, to our ideas, the least pleasing portion of her globe.

An inhabitant of the regions near either pole has to endure extremes of heat and cold, such as would suffice to destroy nearly every race of living beings subsisting upon the earth. During the summer the sun circles continually close to the point overhead, so that, day after day, he pours down his rays with an intensity of heat and of light exceeding nearly twofold the midday light and heat of our own tropical sun. Only for a short time, in autumn and in spring, does the sun rise and set in these regions. A spring

nomical works, the inclination of the earth's axis to her orbit is given as $23\frac{1}{2}°$; were this the case, the larger part of the earth would be uninhabitable.

[1] If the observations of De Vico may be trusted, the inclination of Venus, though less than 75°, is still so considerable (about 55°) as to justify the general conclusions deduced in the following paragraphs.

or autumn day, like one of our days at those seasons, lasts about twelve hours; but the sun attains at noon, in spring or autumn, a height of only a few degrees above the horizon. Then presently comes on the terrible winter, lasting about three of our months, but far more striking in its characteristics even than the long winter night of our polar regions. For, near our poles, the sun approaches the horizon at the hour corresponding to noon; and though he does not show his face, he yet lights up the southern skies with a cheering twilight glow. But during the greater part of the long night of Venus's polar regions the sun does not approach within many degrees of the horizon. Nay, he is further below the horizon than the midnight sun of our arctic regions. Thus, unless the skies are lighted up with auroral splendors, an intense darkness prevails during the polar winter, which must add largely to the horrors of that terrible season. Certainly, none of the human races upon our earth could bear the alternations between these more than polar terrors and an intensity of summer heat far exceeding any with which we are familiar on earth.

Let us see whether the equatorial regions are more pleasing abodes.

In these parts of Venus there are two summers, corresponding to the spring and autumn of the polar regions. At these seasons the sun rises day after day to the point overhead, and the weather corresponds for a while to that which prevails in the tropical regions of our own earth. But between these seasons the sun passes away alternately to the northern and southern skies. During the season corresponding to summer, he is above the horizon nearly throughout the twenty-three and a third hours of Venus's day;[1] but he attains no great elevation, travelling always in a small circle close around the northern pole. During the season corresponding to winter, he is above the horizon only a very short time each day,[2] and is always close to the south, attaining only an elevation of a few degrees at noon. Thus we have the following curious succession of seasons: At the vernal equinox a summer much warmer than our tropical summers; about fifty-six days later, or at the

---

[1] On the equator itself, as on our own, the day is always equal in length to the night. The above account corresponds to a place near the borders of the equatorial zone.

[2] In Admiral Smyth's "Celestial Cycle," the only work in which, so far as I am aware, the effects of the inclination ascribed to Venus's axis have been at all considered, it is stated that in the year of Venus there are but nine and a quarter of her days, "reckoned by the sun's rising and setting, owing to which the sun must appear to pass through a whole sign in little more than three-quarters of her natural day." He does not give any reasons for this remarkable statement, which most certainly is not correct. In all places outside the arctic circles of Venus, the year contains as many natural days as there have been rotations of Venus, wanting one only (as in the case of our own earth); in the remaining regions there will be more or fewer days, according as the station considered is nearer to or further from the arctic circle. Smyth's remark that the varying amplitude of the sun (his distance, that is, from the east and west points), at rising or setting, would give travellers on Venus readier means than our seamen have, of determining the longitude, is just. But the problems involved must be very difficult, and I wish her mathematicians joy of them. The cadets in our schools and training-ships have an easy time of it, compared with the unfortunate beings who are to officer the ships of Venus—always supposing her axis is inclined as we have been assuming.

summer solstice, weather resembling somewhat the spring of our temperate zones, only that the night is exceedingly short; yet fifty-six days later there is another summer, as terrible as the former; and lastly, at the winter solstice, the days are shorter and the cold probably more intense than in the winter of places near our arctic circles. In such regions the contrasts, rather than either of the extremes of climate, would be most trying to terrestrial races; and it is scarcely too much to say that no races subsisting upon our earth could possibly endure such remarkable changes, succeeding each other so rapidly.

Lastly, the beings who inhabit the wide zones which are at once tropical and arctic have climates ranging between the two limits just considered. If they are near the equatorial regions, they suffer from all the vicissitudes of the equatorial climate, with this further tribulation, that, in midwinter, they do not see the sun even at midday, á circumstance by no means compensated (according to our ideas) by the fact that near the summer solstice the sun does not set. If they are near the polar regions, they have a summer even more terrible than the polar summer, and a winter scarcely less dreary and bitter.

Fortunately for our belief in the habitability of Venus, astronomers are far from accepting with confidence the assertions of those observers who have assigned to Venus an inclination so remarkable. If her inclination should at all resemble the earth's, there is every reason to believe that her physical habitudes also resemble those of the earth. In this case, the argument from analogy, presented in the opening chapter of this work, seems to force upon us the conclusion that she is inhabited; while we may believe, though perhaps with less confidence, that a close resemblance subsists between the creatures which people her surface and those with which we are acquainted.

We have no direct evidence, indeed, on which to ground our belief that the greater proximity of Venus to the sun may not be accompanied by any very remarkable peculiarities in the characteristics of her climate. But we have an indirect argument of some strength. If Venus is much nearer than the earth to the sun, the earth, in turn, is much nearer to the sun than Mars is. Yet, as we shall see in the next chapter, we have clear evidence from telescopic observation, and still clearer evidence as the results of spectroscopic research, that the climatic arrangements on Mars do not differ in any remarkable degree from those of our own earth. It would follow, therefore, as at least probable, that a similar resemblance prevails between the climate of the earth and that of Venus. So that, despite the claim which Dr. Whewell has put in for microscopic animalcules with siliceous coverings as the sole inhabitants of Venus, I can find no reason (if the abnormal axial inclination above considered is once disproved) for denying that she may be the abode of creatures as far advanced in the scale of creation as any which exist upon the earth.

Gravity at the surface of Venus is so nearly equal

to terrestrial gravity, that the difference is altogether
insufficient to introduce any noteworthy effects. The
delicate adjustment of the sap-passages of plants to
the force of terrestrial gravity, which Dr. Whewell
notices in his "Bridgewater Treatise," might indeed
be disturbed, if the earth's gravity were suddenly
made equal to that of Venus. But it would be
strangely to limit our conception of Nature's powers
of adaptation, to suppose that therefore there can be
no vegetation on Venus resembling that with which
we are familiar.

Venus is the only planet the extent of whose atmosphere has been carefully estimated. If Venus
had no atmosphere, she would present, when horned,
a semi-circular convexity; whereas the refractive effects of an atmosphere, by causing the sun to illu-
mine rather more than a full hemisphere, would tend
to lengthen her horns. It has been found that her
convexity when she is horned exceeds a semicircle,
and, from the observed extent of this excess, it has
been calculated that her atmosphere is so far more
extensive than ours as to make its refractive effects
on a body near the horizon about one-third greater.
So that, as this is about the proportion in which the
diameter of the sun as seen from Venus exceeds that
which he presents to us, the inhabitant of Venus, like
the inhabitant of our earth, sees the sun fully raised
above the horizon at the moment when, but for re-
fraction, his orb would be just concealed beneath it.

Of the constitution of the atmosphere of Venus
we know little. The spectrum of her light shows

the dark lines which belong to the solar spectrum, and the Padre Secchi has noticed certain faint lines, which seem to indicate the presence of aqueous vapor in the atmosphere of the planet. But he scarcely gives satisfactory evidence that the lines he has thus seen were not due to the absorption exercised by aqueous vapor in our own atmosphere. The same observer finds, in the strengthening of the nitrogen lines near the F line of the spectrum, evidence that the atmosphere of Venus is constituted very similarly to the air we breathe.

On the whole, the evidence we have points very strongly to Venus as the abode of living creatures not unlike the inhabitants of earth. With the sole exception of the inclination, which has been, without sufficient evidence, assigned to the planet's equator, I can see nothing which can reasonably be held to point to an opposite conclusion. Certainly the strong light which the sun pours upon Venus need least of all be objected to, since, if there is one adaptative power which Nature exhibits more clearly than another, it is that by which the various creatures we are acquainted with are enabled to live in comfort under all degrees of light, from the obscurity in which the mole pursues his subterranean researches, to the blazing light of the noonday sun toward which (in fable, if not in .fact) the eagle turns his unshrinking eyes.

There is one peculiarity which yet remains to be noticed. Many are disposed to find, in the beauty of the celestial objects which deck the skies of differ-

ent planets, a certain proof that reasoning beings
must exist who can appreciate the display. Surely
the argument has very little force, since we know
that myriads on myriads of ages must have passed,
during which the glories of our own heavens were
displayed, night after night, with none to regard
them. The moon has passed through all her phases,
the star of morning and of eve has shed its soft
radiance upon the terrestrial landscape, Jupiter and
Saturn have pursued their stately courses among the
fixed stars, and the glories of those constellations
which shine with equal splendor upon all the planets
of the solar scheme have been displayed in all their
unchanging magnificence, while as yet our earth was
the abode but of hideous reptiles, or of yet more
monstrous creatures in forest and in plain.

If this argument were really of force, doubtless
there are no planets in the whole range of the solar
system to which it might not be applied. Each has
some special object of beauty in its heavens, which
is not exhibited to the rest. Certainly Mercury and
Venus are no exceptions to this rule. The inhabitant
of Mercury sees in Venus an orb which, when favorably situated, far outshines in splendor the brightest
of the planetary orbs seen in our skies. So far, indeed, as light-giving power is concerned, Venus must
be no contemptible moon to the Mercurials when she
is nearly in opposition. Our earth, too, with its
companion moon, must form a noble object in the
sky of Mercury, though, without telescopic aid, the
moon perhaps may not be separately visible. To

the inhabitants of Venus, Mercury and the earth must be splendid objects. The former would not only appear much larger than to ourselves, but, being seen almost as favorably as we see Venus, would form a much more striking object in the morning or evening sky of that planet. The earth, as seen by the inhabitants of Venus, must shine much more splendidly than Jupiter does in our skies. Our moon must be distinctly visible, so that, without the aid of any telescope, the inhabitant of Venus has such evidence of the Copernican theory as would suffice, if properly handled, to rout the ranks of the Ptolemaists, supposing there have ever been people in Venus foolish enough to imagine the tiny globe they live upon to be the centre of the universe.

CHAPTER IV

MARS, THE MINIATURE OF OUR EARTH

IT is singular that, among all the orbs which circle around the sun, one only, and that almost the least of the primary planets, should exhibit clearly and unmistakably the signs which mark a planet as the abode of life. We have examined Mercury and Venus, the only other orbs which belong, like the earth and Mars, to the scheme of the minor planets, and we have found little to guide us to any certain conclusion respecting their physical habitudes. When we pass beyond the wide gap which separates the minor planets from the giant members of the solar family, we shall find much to attract our admiration, much to force upon us the belief that these orbs have been created to be the abodes of even nobler races than those which subsist upon our earth; but we shall find little to justify us in asserting that they resemble the earth in those habitudes which seem essential to the wants of terrestrial races. The planet Mars, on the other hand, exhibits in the clearest manner the traces of adaptation to the wants of living beings such as we are

(100)

acquainted with. Processes are at work out yonder
in space which appear utterly useless, a real waste
of Nature's energies, unless, like their correlatives on
earth, they subserve the wants of organized beings.

I would not indeed insist, as some have done, too
strongly upon this argument. I know that on every
side we see tokens of an exuberant activity in Nature, which, according to our ideas, may appear to
savor of wastefulness. The cloud which has been
raised by the solar energies from tropical seas, and
which the winds have wafted over continents, may
shed its waters on the sea or in the desert, where
seemingly they are wholly wasted. Winds may
spend their force apparently in vain. And in a
thousand ways Nature's busy forces may be at work
where we, in our short-sightedness, can see no useful purpose which they subserve.

But there is a marked distinction between such
apparent instances of wasteful action, and the systematic processes which are taking place over the
globe of Mars.

Little as we can appreciate the real character of
Nature's work upon our earth, we can yet dimly
trace out a necessity (depending upon the order
which actually exists) for that which yet appears to
resemble waste. We see, for instance, that if a
country or a continent is to be provided with a due
supply of rain, without supernatural intervention at
every step of the process, that result can only be
secured by what may be described as a random distribution, involving always what to us resembles

waste. If, out of a thousand showers, ten only fall so as to be useful to the land, the object of Nature is subserved, and the useful rainfalls serve to explain the seemingly wasted ones. In reality, of course, there has not been a random distribution, nor has there been any waste; I infer, merely, that a sort of purpose is, in such a case, dimly seen, even by man, who can see so short a distance into the workings of the Almighty.

But in the case of Mars we have no such explanation of the processes we observe, if we dismiss our belief that he is the abode of living creatures. For if Mars be, indeed, untenanted by any forms of life, then these processes going on year after year, and century after century, represent an exertion of Nature's energies which appears absolutely without conceivable utility. If one cloud, out of a hundred of those which shed their waters upon Mars, supplies in any degree the wants of living creatures, then the purport of those clouds is not unintelligible; but if not a single race of beings peoples that distant world, then indeed we seem compelled to say that, in Mars at least, Nature's forces are wholly wasted. Such a conclusion, however, the true philosopher would not care needlessly to adopt.

Let us consider what astronomy has taught us respecting the ruddy planet.

The globe of Mars is about five thousand miles in diameter, so that his linear dimensions bear to those of the earth the proportion of about five to eight. His surface, therefore, is less than that of the earth in the proportion of about twenty-five to sixty-four, or, more exactly (and more conveniently), the surface of the earth is two and a half times as extensive as that of Mars.

The substance of Mars has an average density rather less than three-fourths of our earth's, or very nearly four times that of water. Thus gravity at his surface is much less than terrestrial gravity. It is, in fact, even less than gravity at the surface of Mercury, insomuch that one of our pound weights placed at the surface of Mars would weigh but 6 ozs. 3 dwts., instead of nearly seven ounces as on Mercury. I have already dwelt on the effects of such a relation as this, and shall have occasion, when describing the habitudes of Jupiter, to discuss the converse relation. But I may remark, in passing, how singular it is that we should be compelled to people the smallest planets with the largest inhabitants, if we wish to bring the inhabitants of different orbs to about the same scale of activity. A Daniel Lambert on Mars would be able to leap easily to a height of five or six feet, and he could run faster than the best of our terrestrial athletes. A man of his weight, but proportioned more suitably for athletic exercises, could leap over a twelve-foot wall. On the other hand, a light and active stripling removed to Jupiter would be scarcely able to move from place to place. On the sun his own weight would simply crush him to death.

Mars travels in an orbit of considerable eccentricity; in fact, the centre of his orbit is no less than thirteen millions of miles from the sun. Accordingly, the light and heat he receives from that luminary vary to an important extent. In fact, he gets about half as much heat and light again when in perihelion as when in aphelion. This circumstance affects to an important extent the climatic relations of his two hemispheres, as we shall presently see.

When Mars is at his mean distance from the sun, the light and heat he receives are less than ours in the proportion of about four to nine. The length of his year also constitutes a noteworthy circumstance in which his habitudes differ from those of our earth. His year contains very nearly six hundred and eighty-seven of our days, so that each of the Martial quarters lasts about five and two-thirds of our months. But, owing to the eccentricity of his orbit, the winter and summer of the northern and southern hemispheres are not equal. The Martial day is nearly forty minutes longer than ours.[1]

His equator is inclined at an angle of about twenty-seven and a quarter degrees to the plane of his orbit, and as the corresponding inclination in the case of the earth is about twenty-three and a half degrees, it will be seen that his seasonal changes do not differ much in character, so far at least as they depend on inclination, from our own.

---

[1] More exactly, the length of the Martial day is 24h. 37m. 22.735s. This estimate I have obtained by comparing pictures taken by Hooke in 1666, and by Dawes and Browning in 1866–1869—with precautions sufficing to secure that no complete rotation should anywhere be lost sight of.

The axis of Mars is so situated that the summer of his northern hemisphere occurs when he is at his greatest distance from the sun. The same relation holds in the case of the earth, the sun being one million five hundred thousand miles nearer to us in winter than in summer, whereas, to those who live in the southern hemisphere, he approaches nearer in summer than in winter. But the effects resulting from the relation in the case of Mars must be very much more striking than those we recognize. For, whereas the sun gives only one-fifteenth more heat to the whole earth in January than he does in July, the sun of Mars gives half as much light again in perihelion as in aphelion. The summer of the northern hemisphere of Mars must be rendered much cooler and the winter much warmer by this arrangement. On the other hand, the contrast between the summer and winter of the southern hemisphere is rendered more striking than it otherwise would be.

It is, however, the telescopic aspect of Mars, rather than relations such as we have been dealing with, that affords the most interesting evidence respecting the fitness of the planet to be the abode of living creatures. Although the least but one among the primary planets—a mere speck compared with Jupiter and Saturn—Mars has been examined more minutely and under more favorable circumstances than any object in the heavens except the moon. He does not approach us so closely as Venus, nor does his disk appear so large as Jupiter's, yet he is seen more favorably than the former planet, and on a larger scale, in reality, than the latter. In fact, whereas Venus is one of the most unsatisfactory of all telescopic objects, Mars is one of the most pleasing; and, whereas Jupiter is always more than three hundred and eighty millions of miles from us, Mars sometimes approaches us within less than forty millions of miles.

Yet even this distance is enormous, and it affords high evidence of the skill with which modern telescopes are constructed and used, that astronomers should have been able to span that mighty gulf, and to bring from beyond it reliable information respecting the structure of so distant a world.

Such information has been brought, however, and is full of interest.

Viewed with the naked eye, the most remarkable feature Mars presents is his ruddy color. In the telescope this color is not lost, but, instead of characterizing the whole surface of the planet, it is confined to particular regions—the intermediate parts being for the most part darker, and of a somewhat greenish hue. But a noteworthy feature adds largely to the beauty of the picture presented by the globe of Mars. Two bright spots of white light are seen on opposite sides of his disk, presenting precisely such an appearance as we might imagine the snowy poles of our earth to exhibit to an astronomer on the planet Venus.

Toward the edge of the disk, the ruddy and the greenish tracts are lost in a misty whiteness, which grows gradually brighter up to the very border of

the planet. We shall presently see that this peculiarity, rightly understood, is one of the most instructive features of the planet's aspect.

No telescopist has yet been able to recognize a
satellite attending on the Planet of War.

It was discerned, more than two hundred years
ago, that the reddish spots on Mars, and the darker
regions which lie between them, are not accidental
or variable phenomena, but represent permanent peculiarities of the Martial surface. Cassini, with one of
those outrageously long telescopes which were used
before the invention of achromatic refractors, was
the first to discover this. But the ingenious Hooke
seems to have obtained better views of Mars in
1666. At least, his pictures of the planet are the
only ones taken in the seventeenth century, in which
I can recognize the now well-known aspect of the
Martial continents and oceans.

Since then, Maraldi and the Herschels, Arago,
Secchi, Kunowski, Beer and Mädler, and a host of
other eminent astronomers, have not thought the
study of the planet's aspect beneath their notice.
Within the last few years, also, this work has been
prosecuted by Nasmyth and Jacob, Delarue and
Phillips, and finally and most successfully by Lockyer and Dawes. The last-named observer, especially, whose acuteness of vision earned for him the
title of the eagle-eyed, took so many and such admirable views of the planet as to render it possible
to form a globe of Mars. Sir William Herschel had
charted the planet, and Messrs. Beer and Mädler had

made improved Martial maps; while Professor Phillips, from observations made by himself and Mr.
Lockyer, had constructed two globes of Mars in
which many features were presented. But Mr.
Dawes's pictures of the planet were sufficient, when
carefully compared, for the formation of a globe in
which no large area of the planet should be left
bare of details. He intrusted to me no less than
twenty-seven drawings of Mars, the choicest speci-
mens of a very large series, that I might chart the
planet from them. The accompanying chart of Mars,
in which the darker (black) parts of the planet are
assumed to be seas, and the reddish (white) tracts
continents, exhibits the results obtained from the
study of the complete series. This chart is on the
stereographic projection, and is inverted—the south
polar regions, that is, are at the top—because the
telescopes commonly used by observers exhibit inverted views of the celestial objects.[1] At the top
of the map we see the icy region which lies at the
southern pole of Mars. Around that region is a sea
unnamed in the map. Then along the southern temperate zone there lie several tracts of Martial land,
named after Cassini, Lockyer, and other astronomers.
These regions appear to form a continuous land-belt
round the temperate zone; though there is some un-
certainty on this point, owing to the fact that the
coast-line is not often very distinctly visible. We

---

[1] Mr. Browning, F.R.A.S., has formed a globe of Mars from my
chart, and publishes an interesting series of photographs of this globe
which give fine stereoscopic effects.

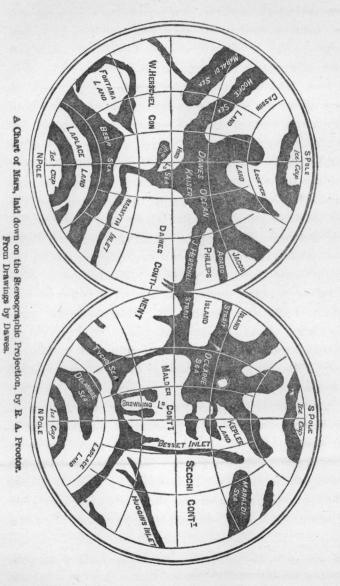

A Chart of Mars, laid down on the Stereographic Projection, by R. A. Proctor. From Drawings by Dawes.

now approach, however, a part of the map where all the features are thoroughly recognized and permanent. Next to the circle of land just described, there is a nearly complete circle of water, one strip only of land connecting the equatorial continents of Mars with the south-temperate zone of minor continents. Beginning at the eastern or left-hand extremity of the map, we have a long sea, called Maraldi Sea, parallel to which runs Hooke Sea, trending in a northwesterly direction, and so running into Dawes Ocean; still further west are two vast islands, called Jacob Island and Phillips Island, between which runs Arago Strait. Beyond these islands lies Delarue Ocean, communicating by narrow straits with two strikingly similar seas. Here the zone of water ends, and we have only to note further, respecting it, that in Delarue Ocean there is a large island, which presents so strikingly brilliant an aspect that it has been supposed to be covered (ordinarily) with snow. It has been called Dawes's Ice Island.

I now come to the most remarkable feature of the Martial geography—or perhaps I ought rather to say, *areography*. This is the great equatorial zone of continents. There are four of these. On the left of the map is Herschel I. Continent. Next is Dawes Continent, the largest of the four, and separated from the former by a long sea called Kaiser Sea. This sea is one of the most striking marks on the planet, and has been recognized from the earliest days of telescopic observation. It is connected toward the east with a flask-shaped sea, somewhat resembling the two which lie at the western extremity of the zone of water just described. At its northernmost end it turns sharply westward, and forms the southern boundary of Dawes Continent. Further west lies Mädler Continent, separated from Dawes Continent by a long strait, which runs almost directly north and south. Lastly, there is Secchi Continent, separated from Mädler Continent by Bessel Inlet and from Herschel Continent by Huggins Inlet. A large lake on the last-named continent is worthy of notice on account of its singular shape. It consists of two bell-shaped seas connected by a narrow and sharply-curved strait.

The northern half of Mars has not been so thoroughly examined as the southern, for a reason which will presently be mentioned. It is known, however, that, in all essential respects, it resembles the southern hemisphere. Next to the equatorial zone of continents there comes a zone of water, expanding at one point into Beer Sea, and at another into Tycho Sea. Then comes a zone of land, called Laplace Land, in which lies an enormous lake called Delambre Sea. Next is a narrow zone of water called the Schröter Sea, and so we reach the north-polar ice-cap.

I have been speaking of the spots on Mars as though they undoubtedly represented land and water. But many may be disposed to question the evidence we have on this point—to ask why the ruddy spots should be held to be continents or islands, and the greenish-colored markings to be oceans, seas, and lakes. We know that, for a long time after the in-

vention of the telescope, astronomers called the darker
portions of the moon *seas*.   They spoke of the Sea
of Serenity, the Sea of Crises, the Sea of Humors,
and so on, and we now know for certain that these
dusky regions are not seas.   It may be asked, therefore, how we can feel certain that the dark spots on
Mars are oceans.

At first sight, this question seems a difficult one
to answer.   The most powerful telescopes have been
directed toward the moon, without affording any satisfactory information respecting the condition of its
surface.   Mars, therefore, which lies—even under the
most favorable circumstances—more than one hundred and sixty times further from us than the moon,
might be thought to be altogether beyond the reach
of our telescopists—so far, at least, as any knowledge
of the Martial surface is concerned.   But one important distinction between Mars and the moon must be
carefully attended to.   The surface of the moon is
always the same—no natural processes seem ever to
take place over that scene of desolation, though the
moon is exposed to contrasts of temperature, compared with which the distinction between the in-
tensest heat of our summers and the bitterest cold
of our winters seems altogether evanescent.   But, on
Mars, the case is certainly different.   Whatever opinion we may form respecting Martial habitudes, whether
we assume or not that Mars is the abode of any forms
of animal life, there can be no question whatever that
physical processes of change are taking place on a
grand scale in that distant world.   Many evidences of

this can be at once adduced. We have spoken of
the Martial features as constant. They differ, for instance, from the markings on Jupiter, which are as
changeful as the aspect of our April skies. But
though the same marking may have been seen by
Hooke in 1666, by Maraldi in 1720, by Herschel in
1780, by Beer and Mädler in 1830–37, and by Dawes
in 1852–65, yet it by no means follows that it is always visible when the part of Mars to which it belongs is turned toward us. A veil is sometimes drawn
over it for hours or even days together. And this
veil has nothing to do with the distinctness or indis-
tinctness with which our own atmosphere permits us
to see the planet. A spot will be blurred and indistinct when a neighboring marking is exhibited with
unusual clearness.

Let us consider an instance of this peculiarity.
On October 3, 1862, Mr. Lockyer was observing
Mars late in the evening. He noticed that a part
of Dawes Ocean, where it borders on Herschel Continent, was hidden from view. In place of the ordinarily dark aspect of this region, a faint, misty
light, with ill-defined borders, was observable. As
the evening progressed, he noticed that the outlines
gradually became clearer, but, when he gave up observation (at about half-past eleven), the white light
still continued to veil the outline of a part of Dawes
Ocean. Now, Mr. Dawes observed Mars on the same
night, at a quarter-past twelve. The drawing which
he took at that hour shows that the process of clearing up, noticed by Mr. Lockyer as being in progress

in the earlier part of the night, had, by the time Mr. Dawes began work, entirely lifted off the veil which concealed the coast-line. The remains of the misty light seen by Lockyer are still to be detected in Mr. Dawes's drawing, but they have passed further south, and no longer hide the shores of Dawes Ocean.

The Padre Secchi, of the Collegio Romano, states that he has often noticed similar appearances, while observing Mars with the fine refractor in the observatory of that institution.

But yet another peculiarity of the same sort remains to be mentioned. Mars, as I have said, has his winter and summer seasons. Since we know the position of the Martial equator upon his surface, we can tell what season is in progress in either hemisphere at any given time. Now, it has been noticed that, when it is winter in one hemisphere, and therefore summer in the other, the former hemisphere is nearly always hidden from view by just such a veil as I have spoken of above.

I may remark, in passing, that this peculiarity has led many observers to form very erroneous impressions respecting the distribution of land and water over the surface of Mars. Seeing one hemisphere covered for weeks together with whitish light, they have concluded that there are no oceans there; and if they have no other opportunity of observing the planet, the mistaken impression remains, and is published to the world with all the authority of the observer's name.

Now, what is this veil which, sometimes for a few hours or days, at others for months together, is drawn over the features of the Martial globe? Have we any terrestrial analogies, by means of which we may interpret this phenomenon?

To answer these questions, let us conceive the case of an observer on Venus watching our earth. Would such an observer always see the features of this globe with equal distinctness? When heavy masses of cloud are drawn over a wide expanse of country—spreading often, as meteorologists record, for hundreds and even thousands of miles—can we suppose that the astronomer on Venus could pierce through the veil? Since we cannot see the bright body of the sun through a dense cloud-veil, we may be certain that the observer on Venus cannot see the oceans and continents of our earth when thus cloud-shadowed. So far as the cloud-veil extends, the lands and seas of this globe would be to him, at such a time, as though they were not.

Here, then, we have an argument from analogy for supposing that the veil, which from time to time conceals the Martial features, may resemble terrestrial cloud-banks. Let us next inquire whether there is anything in the behavior of the Martial veil to justify this view.

It is clear that, if we held the concealing medium to be of a cloudy nature, the disappearance of the features of the hemisphere which is passing through the Martial winter would indicate that in winter the Martial skies are more clouded than in summer.

We know that this is the case on our own earth—
that fogs and mists, clouds, rain, and snow, are
phenomena far more frequently observed in winter
than in summer. We know also why it is so. The
cold winter air is unable to retain the aqueous vapor
continually passing into it, and is thus forced to pre-
cipitate this vapor in one or other of the forms just
named. Nor can we see any reason why the Martial
atmosphere, supposing it to resemble our own,
should not act in precisely the same manner. Thus
we recognize, in the remarkable seasonal peculiarity
above described, what seems to be the exact counterpart of processes recognized upon the earth.

And though I admit that there is considerable
objection to the mode of argument I am next going
to make use of, yet, as it is one which has great
weight with many minds, and is not without its own
peculiar force, I feel justified in applying it as a
subsidiary support to the views I am discussing. It
is known that the peculiarities which characterize
terrestrial atmospheric phenomena tend in an important manner to mitigate the extremes of summer and
winter temperature. The clouds which hang over
our winter skies, far from acting to increase the
coldness of winter through their effect in keeping
off the sun's rays, in reality represent an enormous
supply of heat brought from warmer parts of the
earth, and liberated for our benefit as the invisible
vapor of water assumes the form of cloud or rain.
And although these processes are strictly in accordance with natural laws, yet we are justified in recog-

nizing them as evidences of the beneficence of the Almighty. Now, on Mars, we may be sure, the winters tend to be far more bitter than ours, partly because of his greater distance from the sun, but chiefly because of the more marked contrast existing between his various seasons. Hence, if there are living creatures on Mars, it can scarcely be doubted that an arrangement such as that which prevails on earth is yet more necessary to the welfare of the Martialists. Thus, we derive an argument from the *a priori* consideration of the nature of Martial requirements, to favor our interpretation of the phenomena actually observed.

Perhaps the reader may be disposed to inquire whether the clearing up of a portion of the Martial disk observed by Lockyer and Dawes admits of interpretation in a similar way. To this it may be replied that, from the observed position of the region in question, the Martial *time of day* there must have been somewhere about noon when Mr. Lockyer began his observations, and about one o'clock in the afternoon (according to our terrestrial mode of reckoning) when Mr. Dawes observed the planet. It is no uncommon thing to see our terrestrial skies clear up soon after midday; and if the veil which conceals the Martial features is really cloudy, this is precisely what happened out yonder, forty millions of miles away from us, on the day in question.

I think the reader will at least concede that the explanation here given of these peculiarities is more natural than one which was put forward some time since by an eminent French astronomer. He urged that Martial vegetation, instead of being green like ours, is red; hence in the Martial summer the surface, as seen by us, assumes a ruddy aspect, while the wintry hemisphere loses its ruddy tint. According to this interpretation, such changes as were noticed by Secchi would indicate the sudden blooming forth of Martial vegetation over hundreds of square miles of the Martial surface.

To the evidence already dealt with may be added that which is afforded by the whiteness of the disk of Mars near the edge. Knowing that the parts of Mars which thus appear concealed in mist are those where it is morning or evening to the Martialists, we see a close analogy here to terrestrial relations, since our own skies are commonly more moisture-laden in the morning and evening than near midday.[1]

I may here pause, in passing, to notice under what difficulties the observation of Mars is conducted by the terrestrial observer. To begin with, the sky must be exceptionally clear; and none but the practiced observer knows how seldom there occurs what is called "a good observing night." Then it must be *a fine day for the Martialists*, for clouds over

---

[1] In the "Popular Science Review" for January, 1869, I have indicated a subsidiary explanation of this peculiarity, founded on the probable shape of the Martial clouds. For the same reason that, near the horizon, our own cumulus clouds seem more closely packed than overhead, the Martialists would see a clearer sky overhead than near the horizon. It follows, at once, that we should see those parts of the surface of Mars best which we look upon in a nearly vertical direction, that is, the central parts of his disk.

Mars, or even an imperfectly clear atmosphere, must produce quite as bad an effect in spoiling the definition of Martial features as similar phenomena on earth. Again, Mars only comes into a favorable position once in every two and a quarter years, continuing to be well placed for only a few months. Thus it happens that, although Mars has been telescopically observed for more than two hundred years, the actual time during which he has been favorably placed for observation has been very much less; and, taking into account all the requirements for good definition, it may be said that Mars has not been under really effective observation for more than a very few days.

Of course, if we admit that the vaporous envelope which occasionally hides parts of Mars is aqueous, we must believe in the existence of oceans upon Mars. And, from our knowledge of the appearance of our own seas, we should immediately recognize the greenish parts of Mars as the Martial oceans, and look upon the ruddy parts as continents. We have seen that the behavior of the vaporous envelopes corresponds to that of our own clouds and fogs. But it might be thought possible that the vapors arise from fluids other than water; that, in fact, a state of things exists upon Mars wholly different from that which prevails upon our own earth.

Ten years ago it would have been very difficult to disprove such an argument as this, however *bizarre* it may seem. But the wonderful powers of the spectroscope have been applied to this question, and there is no mistaking the results which have been obtained. We must premise that this is hardly a favorable case for the application of spectroscopic analysis, which (as available to the astronomer) deals most effectively with self-luminous objects. Still, there was a possibility that the light which comes from Mars might have been so acted upon by vapors in the Martial atmosphere, that its spectrum would be affected in an appreciable manner.

Mr. Huggins examined Mars in 1864 without satisfactory results, but at the opposition of Mars in 1867 he was more successful. In the following description of his most striking observation I epitomize his account: On February 14th he examined Mars with a spectroscope attached to his powerful eight-inch refractor. The rainbow-colored streak was crossed, near the orange part, by groups of dark lines agreeing in position "with lines which make their appearance in the solar spectrum when the sun is low down, so that its light has to traverse the denser strata of our atmosphere." To determine whether these lines belonged to the light from Mars or were caused by our own atmosphere, Mr. Huggins turned his spectroscope toward the moon, which happened to be nearer the horizon than Mars, so that the atmospheric lines would be stronger in the moon's spectrum than in that of the planet. But the group of lines referred to was not visible in the lunar spectrum. Hence it was clear that they belong to the Martial atmosphere, and not to ours.

I have said that these lines appear in the solar

spectrum when the sun is shining through the denser strata of our atmosphere. Let us consider a moment the light which this fact throws on the nature of the Martial atmosphere. It must contain at least those constituent vapors whose existence in our atmosphere causes the appearance of these lines in the solar spectrum. Hence there must be *some* similarity between the Martial atmosphere and our own. But we know, from the researches of the Padre Secchi, that it is the aqueous vapor in our air which causes the appearance of the lines in question. Hence there must be aqueous vapor in the Martial atmosphere.

This discovery at once justifies the title of the present chapter. Let us consider what a number of interesting results follow from it.

The water in the Martial air must be raised from seas and rivers upon the planet. These, therefore, consist of water and not of other fluids. The two white spots, then, on the Martial disk are no longer doubtful appearances. Before the discovery that water exists on Mars, it was perhaps somewhat bold to pronounce that these spots certainly indicate the presence of ice-fields around the Martial poles, resembling those which exist around the poles of the earth. Sir William Herschel, indeed, with that confidence which he always showed when he had a trustworthy analogy to guide him, came to this conclusion on the strength of the correspondence between the changes of the two spots and the progress of the Martial seasons. But many astronomers felt that there was still room to doubt whether we could really speak of the spots as

"The snowy poles of moonless Mars."

Now, however, we know that they can be no other than snow-caps. Nay, if Mars were so far off that we could not distinguish these spots, we could yet, on the strength of what the spectroscope has taught us, pronounce confidently that his polar regions must be ice-bound.

Let us proceed a step or two further. We have seen that there are oceans on Mars; we know that clouds and vapors rise from those oceans and are wafted over his continents; and, finally, we have learned that snow falls on the Martial polar regions. These things are very interesting in themselves, but they indicate the occurrence of processes yet more interesting. The formation and the dissipation of clouds are among the most important of all the processes by which Nature arranges and modifies the temperature of our earth. The heat of the sun's rays is used up, so to speak, in raising aqueous vapor from the surface of the ocean. Thus the air is rendered cooler than it otherwise would be, and this takes place just where coolness is most needed. But the aqueous vapor, once raised, is swept by the winds to other regions. So long as the air remains warm, the aqueous vapor remains unchanged; but, so soon as it has been carried to colder regions, it is condensed into the form of cloud or mist, and while changing to this form it parts with the heat which had turned it into vapor. Thus where heat is in excess, it is used up in forming aqueous vapor, and where heat is wanted there the aqueous vapor distributes it.

We see, then, that on Mars there exists the same admirable contrivance for tempering climates which we find on our own earth.

But let us consider yet another office fulfilled by aqueous vapor. It not only serves to convey the heat from the warmer parts of the earth to those regions where heat is most needed. It forms clouds which serve to shelter the earth from the sun's heat by day, and to prevent the escape of the earth's heat by night, which also, in refreshing rains, "drop fatness on the earth." Now, the clouds on Mars are certainly dissipated in some way, because, as I have said, astronomers have repeatedly seen them disappear. And doubtless, like our own clouds, they are often dissipated by the sun's heat. But we may take it for granted that, like our terrestrial clouds, they are also often dissipated by falling in rain. Thus the Martial lands are nourished by refreshing rainfalls; and who can doubt that they are thus nourished for the same purpose as our own fields and forests—namely, that vegetation of all sorts may grow abundantly?

But yet, again, the transit of clouds from place to place implies the existence of aërial currents. Clouds cannot, indeed, even form and be dissipated without occasioning wind-currents; and it need hardly be said that the Martial clouds could not be carried to his polar regions, there to fall in snow, unless the atmospheric currents on Mars were extensive and persistent. We see, then, that Mars has winds as our earth has. Doubtless his trade-winds are less marked than ours, because his surface rotates less rapidly than the earth's, his globe being much smaller, while his rotation-period is slightly greater. But he has less need for trade-winds, his oceans being so much less extensive than ours. No Columbus on Mars has ever needed the persistent breath of easterly winds to encourage him on his voyage to an undiscovered continent. Rather, the intricate navigation of the narrow Martial seas would be favored by variable breezes. But the great purposes which the circulation of our own atmosphere subserves are carried out efficiently out yonder on Mars. The air is cleansed and purified, its thermal and electrical conditions are regulated, clouds are wafted from place to place; and, in fine, the atmosphere is rendered fit for all those purposes for which, like our own, it has doubtless been created.

We may trace yet further, however, the results which flow from the existence of aqueous vapor in the atmosphere of Mars. We see the polar snows aggregating in the Martial winter and diminishing in the Martial summer. And we know that, on our own earth, the increase and the diminution of the polar snows are processes intimately associated with the formation and maintenance of the oceanic circulation. Doubtless much yet remains to be done before that system of circulation will be fully understood. The rival views which have been maintained by Sir John Herschel and Captain Maury have served to throw a certain air of doubt over the theory of ocean-currents.[1] But whether we ascribe the equatorial currents of our oceans to the trade-winds with Herschel, or to differences of specific gravity with Maury, we see that, in the first place, both causes operate in the case of Mars, and secondly, that the submarine return-currents from our polar regions must, at any rate, be due to the presence of ice in the polar seas. So that undoubtedly the Martial oceans, so far as their peculiar conformation will permit, are traversed by currents in various directions and at various depths.

Then, lastly, there must be rivers on Mars. The clouds which often hide from our view the larger part of a Martial continent, indicate a rainfall at least as considerable (in proportion) as that which we have on the earth. The water thus precipitated on the Martial continents can find its way no otherwise to the ocean than along river-courses.

---

[1] If Herschel has completely overthrown Maury's theory that currents are altogether due to differences of specific gravity, saltness, and so on, Maury has at least been as successful in overthrowing Herschel's theory that the currents are due to the trade-winds. A theory more probable than either is, I think, that according to which the whole system of circulation is set in motion by the continual evaporation going on in equatorial seas. Thus, by a process resembling suction, an in-draught of cold water is caused, and this water, coming from higher latitudes, where the earth's eastwardly motion is less, to lower latitudes, where the eastwardly motion is greater, produces the relatively cold and westwardly equatorial currents which exist in the Atlantic, Indian, and Pacific Oceans. Recent researches into the temperature of the deep sea have tended strongly to confirm these views, which I dealt with at some length in the "Intellectual Observer" for May, 1867.

As to the nature of these rivers again, we may form conjectures founded on trustworthy analogies. The mere existence of continents and oceans on Mars proves the action of forces of upheaval and of depression. There must be volcanic eruptions and earthquakes, modelling and remodelling the crust of Mars. Thus there must be mountains and hills, valleys and ravines, water-sheds and water-courses. All the various kinds of scenery which make our earth so beautiful have their representatives in the ruddy planet. The river courses to the ocean, by cataract and lake, here urging its way impetuously over rocks and bowlders, there gliding with stately flow along its more level reaches. The rivulet speeds to the river, the brook to the rivulet, and from the mountain recesses burst forth the refreshing springs which are to feed the Martial brooklets.

Who can doubt what the lesson is that all these things are meant to teach us? So far, let it be remembered, we have been guided onward by no speculative fancies, but simply by sober reasoning. But can we pause just here? Shall we recognize in Mars all that makes our own world so well fitted to our wants—land and water, mountain and valley, cloud and sunshine, rain, and ice, and snow, rivers and lakes, ocean-currents and wind-currents, without believing further in the existence of those forms of life without which all these things would be wasted? Surely, if it is rashly speculative to say of this charming planet that it is the abode of life—if we must, indeed, limit ourselves to the consideration of what has been absolutely seen—it is yet to speculate ten thousand times more rashly to assert, in the face of so many probable arguments to the contrary, that Mars is a barren waste, either wholly untenanted by living creatures, or inhabited by beings belonging to the lowest orders of animated existence.

CHAPTER V

PASSING over the zone of asteroids, we come now to the noblest of all the planets—the giant Jupiter. If bulk is to be the measure of a planet's fitness to be the abode of living creatures, then must Jupiter be inhabited by the most favored races existing throughout the whole range of the solar system. Exceeding our earth some twelve hundred and thirty times in volume, and more than three hundred times in mass, this magnificent orb was rightly selected by Brewster as the crowning proof of the relative insignificance of the earth in the scale of creation — assuming only that we can indeed gauge the purposes of the Creator by the familiar tests of measure and weight.

Or if we estimate Jupiter rather by the forces inherent in his system, if we contemplate the enormous rapidity with which his vast bulk whirls round upon its axis, or trace the stately motion with which he sweeps onward on his orbit, or measure the influences by which he sways his noble family of satellites, we are equally impressed with the feeling that here we

(128)

have the prince of all the planets, the orb which, of all others in the solar scheme, suggests to us conceptions of the noblest forms of life.

The very symmetry and perfection of the system which circles round Jupiter have led many to believe that he must be inhabited by races superior in intelligence to any which people our earth. The motions of these bodies afford indeed to our astronomers a noble subject of study. Our most eminent mathematicians have given many hours of study to the phenomena which the four moons present to the terrestrial observer. But we can trace only the general movements of the satellites of Jupiter. Their minor disturbances, the effects of the varying influences which the sun and Jupiter exert upon them, and which the moons exert upon each other, must tax the powers of far abler mathematicians even than he who "surpassed the whole human race in mental grasp."

But, after all, we must judge of Jupiter rather according to the evidence we have, and the analogies which are most directly applicable to the case, than according to fancies such as these. We know that the sun, which surpasses Jupiter in weight and volume even more than Jupiter surpasses the earth, is yet not the abode of life, so that mere size and mass must not be held to argue habitability. We know that many meteors and comets sweep through spaces more swiftly than the vast bulk of Jupiter, so that the energies indicated by mere velocity of motion, whether orbital or rotational, must be equally disregarded. Nor must we forget that, ages before men

studied the motions of our own moon, she presented
the same noble subject of study that she forms in
our day for an Adams, a Leverrier, or a Delaunay.
Even now a thousand grand problems are presented
to our men of science which escape their notice; and
we might as reasonably argue that there must be
creatures existing unperceived among us, who deal
with these problems, as that, out yonder in space,
there must be beings who study the complicated
motions of the Jovial satellites.

Jupiter presents the following principal physical
habitudes:

He has a diameter of about eighty-five thousand
miles, or nearly eleven times as large as the earth's,
a surface one hundred and fifteen times larger, and,
as I have said, a volume more than twelve hundred
times larger. Gravity at his surface is about two
and a half times as great as on our earth's, so that
such creatures as exist around us would find their
weight much more than doubled if they were removed
to Jupiter. He lies more than five times further from
the sun than our earth, and the light and heat which
he receives from that orb are reduced to about one-
twenty-fifth of our supply. He rotates on his axis
in rather less than ten hours (nine hours, fifty-five
minutes, twenty-six seconds), so that the length of
his day is considerably less than half of ours. His
axis is nearly perpendicular to his orbit, so that
there are no appreciable seasonal changes as he
sweeps round the sun in his long year of 4,332½
days.

It will be convenient to consider, first, the probable influence of the great attractive power of Jupiter upon the dimensions of the various orders of living creatures existing upon his surface.

The grandeur of his orb naturally suggests, at first sight, the idea of beings far exceeding, both in might and bulk, those which live upon the earth. Old Wolfius was led to a similar conclusion in another way. I quote his quaint fancies as quaintly presented by Admiral Smyth. "Wolfius," says the genial sailor, "not only asserts that there are inhabitants in Jupiter, but also shows that they must necessarily be much larger than those of the earth; in fact, that they are of the giant kind, and nearly fourteen feet high by *eye*-measurement. And thus he proves it. It is shown in optics that the pupil of the eye dilates and contracts according to the degree of light it encounters. Wherefore, since in Jupiter the sun's meridian height is much weaker than on the earth, the pupil will need to be much more dilatable in the Jovial creature than in the terrestrial one. But the pupil is observed to have a constant proportion to the ball of the eye, and the ball of the eye to the rest of the body; so that, in animals, the larger the pupil the larger the eye, and consequently the larger the body. Assuming that these conditions are unquestionable, he shows that Jupiter's distance from the sun, compared with the earth's, is as twenty-six to five; the intensity of the sun's light in Jupiter is to its intensity on the earth in a duplicate ratio five to twenty-six." The eyes

of the Jovials and their dimensions generally must
be correspondingly enlarged, and "it therefore follows that even Goliath of Gath would have cut but
a sorry figure among the natives of Jupiter. That
is, supposing the Philistine's altitude to be somewhere between eight feet and eleven, according as
we lean to Bishop Cumberland's calculation, or the
Vatican copy of the Septuagint. Now, Wolfius
proves the size of the inhabitants of Jupiter to be
the same as that of Og, king of Bashan, whose iron
camp-bed was nine cubits in length and four in
breadth—or rather he shows, in the way stated, the
ordinary altitude of the Jovicolæ to be 13 Paris
feet, and the height of Og to have been 13 feet.
See his Works, vol. iii., p. 438."

This exact determination of the dimensions of
Jovial men would be very pleasing and satisfactory,
were it not that another line of argument guides us
at least as conclusively to a very different view. If
we are to assume that beings resembling men in all
attributes except size, actually exist on Jupiter, we
might claim for these beings the power of moving
from place to place as freely as we do, with quite as
much reason as Wolfius claimed for them the same
powers of vision that we possess. Proceeding according to this view, we are led to the conclusion
that the *Jovicolæ* are pygmies about two and a half
feet, on the average, in height. For we know that
a man removed to Jupiter would weigh about two
and a half times as much as he does on our own
earth. He would thus be oppressed with a burden

equivalent to half as much again as his own weight. This would render life itself an insupportable burden; and we have to inquire what difference of size would suffice to make a Joveman as active as our terrestrial men. Now, the weight of bodies similarly proportioned varies as the third power of the height; for example, a body twice as high as another — in other respects similar—will be eight times as heavy. But the muscular power of animals varies as the cross-section of corresponding muscles, or obviously as the square of the linear dimensions; so that of two animals similarly constituted, but one twice as high as the other, the larger would be four times the more powerful. He would weigh, however, eight times as much as the other. He would therefore be only half as active. Similarly, an animal three times as high as another of similar build would be only one-third as active; and so on for all such relations. Now, since a terrestrial man removed to Jupiter would be two and a half times as heavy as on the earth, it follows obviously that a man on Jupiter proportioned like our terrestrial men would be as active as they are, if his height were to theirs as one to two and a half. Hence, setting six feet as the maximum ordinary height of men on the earth, we see that the tallest and handsomest of the Jovicolæ can be but two and a half feet in height, *if only our premises are correct.* Thus, Tom Thumb and other little fellows, if removed to Jupiter, might be wondered at for their enormous height, and eagerly sought after by any Carlylian

Fredericks who may be forming grenadier corps out yonder.

One line of argument having thus led us to regard the Jovicolæ as Ogs of Bashan, while another equally plausible has reduced their dimensions to those of our two-year-old children, we may fairly conclude that this method of reasoning is fallacious. We must not measure the inhabitants of other worlds according to the conceptions suggested by the forms of life we are acquainted with upon earth. We must admit the possibility that arrangements, as different from those we are familiar with as the constitution of the insect is from that of man, may be presented amid the orbs which circle round the sun. It were unwise, no doubt, to give free scope to speculation where we have in truth no means of forming an opinion. We need not imagine, as some have done, that "the inhabitants of Jupiter are bat-winged," or with others, "that they are inveterate dancers." Nor, to take the views of more respectable authorities, need we agree with Sir Humphry Davy, that the bodies of the Jovials are composed of "numerous convolutions of tubes more analogous to the trunk of the elephant than anything else"; with Whewell, that they are pulpy, gelatinous creatures, living in a dismal world of water and ice with a cindery nucleus; nor finally, with Brewster, that the Jovial may have his "home in subterranean cities warmed by central fires, or in crystal caves cooled by ocean-tides, or may float with the Nereids upon the deep, or mount upon wings as eagles, or rise upon the pinions of the dove, that he may flee away and be at rest." So soon as we give a definite form to the conceptions that the imagination, free from the control of exact knowledge, frames respecting the inhabitants of other worlds, we touch at once on the grotesque, the hideous, or the ridiculous.¹ It is sufficient to recognize the probability, or rather the certainty, that the *beings of other worlds are very different from any we are acquainted with, without endeavoring to give shape and form to fancies that have no foundation in fact.

We may regard it as probable, however, that living creatures in Jupiter, if any exist, are built generally on a much smaller scale than those which people our earth. Trees, plants, and the vegetable world generally, must also, one would imagine, be very differently constituted from those we are familiar with. It is well known that the motion of the vegetable juices is in part regulated by the force of

---

¹ It may be worth while to gather a lesson from this circumstance. We know that every form of life is replete with evidences of adaptation (no matter how secured) to the conditions which surround it. We have thus evidenced to us, as forcibly as possible, the perfection of the laws by which the Creator rules the universe, and a measure (if one may so speak) even of that which is inconceivable by us—His infinite wisdom. Now, man, with all his knowledge of the Creator's ways, yet so soon as he passes the boundary of the known, pictures to himself all manner of unnatural and impossible forms of existence. Even the unknown parts of our own earth have been peopled ere now, in imagination, with "men whose heads do grow beneath their shoulders," and other similarly incongruous beings. It is more excusable, perhaps, that an anatomically impossible structure should have been assigned to angels (the cherubim have been even more unfortunate), while the Evil One, that "goeth about as a roaring lion," has had the principal attributes of a class of *ruminantia* assigned to him.

gravity, and therefore it must be admitted that the structure of terrestrial plants is in part dependent upon the value of gravitation at the earth's surface. Whewell, in his "Bridgewater Treatise" on the astronomical evidence of design in Creation, lays great stress on this relation, pointing out, if I remember right, that all vegetation would be destroyed at once if there could suddenly take place any marked change in the earth's attractive forces. If this view is correct, it is certain that none of our plants could thrive on the soil of Jupiter.

The year of Jupiter differs in a much more striking manner than that of Mars from our terrestrial year. It consists of nearly twelve such years as ours, so that the period corresponding to one of our seasons lasts nearly three years, and a Jovial month is nearly equal to one of our terrestrial years. He has, however, no seasons in our sense of the word, since his equator is inclined but little more than three degrees to his orbit. Thus a perpetual spring reigns all over his surface.

But before we proceed to form a high opinion of the planet's condition under the influence of this perpetual spring, let us distinctly understand what the words mean. The word spring has a genial sound to ourselves, because we associate it with that which is commonly the pleasantest portion of our year; but it is just possible that the perpetual spring reigning over Jupiter, though doubtless well adapted to the wants of his inhabitants, leads to a state of things such as we might not find altogether so agreeable.

Admiral Smyth says that "as the rays of the sun fall perpendicularly on the body of the planet,[1] and always continue to do so, the heat must be as nearly as possible equal at all times of the year—a perennial summer: this is a striking display of beneficent arrangement." But we must be cautious in adopting this mode of argument in dealing with the Creator's ways. That the arrangement *is* beneficent, we need not of course question. But that we can recognize the way in which it is beneficent is quite another matter. If Jupiter's great distance from the sun is compensated for by this peculiar disposition of his axis, and we are to admire the beneficence thus displayed, are we therefore to find fault with the Creator for not dealing similarly with Saturn, Uranus, and Neptune, which, being further from the sun, have greater need than Jupiter of some special adap-

---

[1] In the same paragraph Admiral Smyth says that, as seen from Jupiter's equatorial regions, the sun would seem to move through the heavens with great rapidity, while near the polar regions the sun's motion will be comparatively slow, and he will be seen to describe only a small semicircle above the horizon. The direct reverse is, however, the case, the sun's path and the rapidity of his apparent diurnal motion being nearly constant for all parts of Jupiter, and throughout his year. Admiral Smyth seems to have thought that the variations of the sun's path in Jupiter corresponded to those observed in the progress of a year at any place on the earth's equator, the sun always rising vertically and always describing a complete semicircle, though attaining different altitudes at different *seasons*. The real fact is, that in all parts of Jupiter the sun describes a complete diurnal semicircle, attaining a different midday altitude in different *places*. But, as he always rises nearly due east, and sets nearly due west (as he does in spring-time all over the earth), he necessarily crosses the horizon at different angles as seen in different places, and always describes about half of a great circle of the sphere.

tation of the sort? It seems safer to consider the
consequences which flow from the arrangement without any special reference to the design of the Creator
in permitting them, lest, in our over-anxiety to recognize beneficence in the treatment of one world, we
should adopt a mode of reasoning which leads to the
direct conclusion that other worlds have been ill-
cared for.

The great peculiarity resulting from the arrangement in question—the only peculiarity, in fact, of
which we can speak with any confidence—consists in
this, that, everywhere on Jupiter, day and night are
of equal length. It is in this sense only that perpetual spring—or perpetual autumn, if we please—
reigns on the giant planet. The different latitudes
of Jupiter have climates differing quite as much as
those found in different latitudes on our own earth.
At the equator the sun passes every day nearly to
the point overhead. At the poles the sun seems to
glide along the horizon, rising in the east, passing
round—always near the horizon—toward the south,
and thence to his setting-place in the west. In intermediate latitudes, the sun passes to a southerly
elevation which is greater or less, according as the
place is nearer to or further from Jupiter's equator.
It follows that there is a marked difference between
the sub-equatorial and the sub-polar regions in Jupiter, while between these regions every intermediate
climate is to be found.

Owing to the rapidity of Jupiter's rotation, the
motion of the sun in the Jovial sky must be much

more readily discernible and measurable than that
with which the sun seems to pass across our own
heavens. He traverses the whole semicircle, from
the eastern to the western horizon, in two minutes
less than five hours, or about six degrees in ten
minutes. This corresponds to a motion through a
space equal to the sun's diameter (as we see him) in
fifty seconds, and must be readily discernible, even
to the unaided vision of the Jovicolæ, unless their
eyesight is much inferior to ours. The smallness of
the sun, as seen from Jupiter, must help to render
the motion more perceptible. He presents to them
an apparent diameter only equal to about one-fifth
of that with which we see him, so that in ten seconds he seems to pass over a space equal to his own
diameter.

The other celestial bodies are affected with similar
motions as seen from Jupiter. Of course, those seen
near the poles of his heavens seem relatively at rest.
One of these poles lies in the heart of the constellation Draco; the other lies close by the great Magellanic Cloud, which must present a magnificent cyno-
sure to the inhabitants of the southern hemisphere
of the planet. The contrast between the steadfastness of the polar star-groups and the swift motions
of the equatorial constellations must be impressive
indeed. These equatorial groups are no other than
our old friends the zodiacal constellations. As seen
by the inhabitants of Jupiter, they rise with a perceptible but stately motion above the eastern horizon,
pass to their culmination on the southern meridian,

and so to their setting-place in the west—exhibiting the same splendors which the terrestrial astronomer delights to gaze upon, enhanced by the peculiar impressions of active power suggested by visible and obvious motion.

It may seem, at first sight, that the presence of the Jovial satellites must tend to dim the splendor of the sidereal heavens. Our own moon, despite the beautiful passage[1] in which Homer has described the calm beauty of a moonlit night, certainly detracts largely from the magnificence of the star-groups; and as at times there must be four moons visible above the horizon of the Jovials, it might seem that all but the brighter stars would be quite obliterated. The first moon must appear somewhat larger than our own; the next has an apparent diameter rather more than half as large as that of our moon; the third (really the largest) appears about as large as the second; and the fourth has an apparent diameter equal to about a quarter of our moon's. Thus, in all, they cover a space on the sky more than half as large again as that which our moon covers. But, in reality, they cannot have nearly so marked an effect in dimming the lustre of the stars. For it must not be forgotten that they shine only by reflecting the sun's light, and that he illuminates

---

[1] Homer must not be held responsible for Pope's amazing description, which, strangely enough, has found an ardent admirer in one of our best modern observers. Homer did, however, mention, as a characteristic of the moonlit sky, that "all the stars shine," a proof that sometimes, as Horace tells us, the great master nodded.

them but faintly, in comparison with the light he pours upon our own moon. In effect, supposing their reflective capacities equal to the moon's, they must appear less brilliant than she does, in the proportion of about one to twenty-five; and combining this result with the above relation, it follows that, even if they could all be "full" together, they could send to the Jovials but about one-sixteenth part of the light we receive from the full moon. But, as a matter of fact, they cannot all be full together. The motions of the inner three are so related, that, though there is nothing to prevent them from being all visible together,[1] yet, when so visible, one only can be full. The fourth may be full at the same time, or, in fact, may be combined with the other three in any way, since its motions are not bound up with theirs as theirs are *inter se*.

Even now, however, we have not reached a full estimate of the extent of the mistake which those astronomers have made who speak of the splendor with which the satellites of Jupiter illuminate his skies. When at that part of their orbits where they would otherwise be full, the three inner moons are always eclipsed, and though the fourth, by reason of its great distance,[2] sometimes escapes eclipse, yet more frequently it is obscured like the others. The two in-

---

[1] Or all invisible together. Lardner asserts the contrary; so that one would imagine he had never seen all the moons together on the same side of Jupiter.

[2] Not on account of the inclination of its orbit being large, as Sir John Herschel has said. The orbit of this satellite is, indeed, less inclined than the orbits of the others.

ner satellites are eclipsed for upward of two hours,
and as they occupy but a few hours in completing
their circuit round the sky,[1] it will be seen how
largely this relation detracts from their light-supply-
ing powers.

We see, then, that those writers have been mistaken who allege that the great distance of Jupiter
from the sun is compensated by the number of his
moons, and the quantity of light they reflect toward
him. So far is this from being the case, that, under
the most favorable circumstances, they can supply
during the Jovial night but about one-twentieth part
of the light with which the full moon illuminates our
nocturnal skies. The poetical descriptions which im-
aginative writers have indulged in, respecting the
splendor of the scene presented by these satellites,
will not bear the dry light of numerical estimation.
That the satellite-system of Jupiter subserves important functions, and affords, in reality, like all the
works of the Creator, the amplest evidence of design,
need not be questioned; but that we have been able
to understand the special purpose for which they
have been created—in fine, "to see," as the Creator
does, "that they are good"—may be assuredly denied.

Perhaps, if one were able to discuss with advantage the special purposes which this or that portion
of creation is intended to subserve, it might be argued
that the outer planets have greater need of moons than

---

[1] Moving in a direction contrary to that due to the rotation of Jupiter, they of course remain longer above the horizon than the sun, or
the equatorial fixed stars.

the inner, because, their year being longer, there is greater occasion for objects whose motions shall serve as measures of time. The satellites of Jupiter supply, by their separate motions, convenient measures of the shorter time-intervals; while, by their successive conjunctions, (1) in pairs, (2) the three inner together, and (3) the outer with pairs of the inner, they afford convenient measures of longer intervals.

But let us turn from vague guesses at the purposes of the Almighty to the consideration of those facts which are actually presented to our notice.

Recognizing the existence of varied climatic relations in different parts of Jupiter, we have now to consider the climate of the planet generally, to contemplate the position of this great orb in the solar system, and to determine how far its great distance from the sun may be compensated by other relations.

There can be no doubt that the amount of heat poured by the sun on any portion of Jupiter's surface, placed perpendicularly with respect to the heat-rays, must be very much less than the amount received by an equal portion of our earth's surface, similarly situated. The direct heating effects of the sun must, in fact, as already stated, be less on Jupiter than on our own earth, in the proportion of about one to twenty-five. And it cannot be doubted that the effects of this difference must be highly important, whatever arrangements may exist to compensate for the deficiency of heat. If we can demonstrate in any way that the mean temperature of the Jovial atmosphere is equal to that of our own air, or even greater, yet the difference of the sun's direct heat involves a variety of consequences which we cannot disregard.

We know, for instance, that it is principally the direct heat of the sun that causes the evaporation of water from the surface of oceans, seas, lakes, and rivers, and therefore all the important consequences which flow from the presence of aqueous vapor in large quantities in the earth's atmosphere. We can conceive the existence of vapors in the air which might keep away from the earth's surface the greater portion of the sun's heat, and yet, by preventing the escape of the remainder by radiation into space, might leave the general warmth of the air around us as great as it is at present. But it cannot be doubted that such an arrangement would injuriously affect the whole economy of evaporation and its consequences, winds, rains, clouds, mist, with *their* consequences, so important for the welfare of terrestrial races.

And in like manner other effects accruing from the direct action of the solar rays might be considered.

It follows, then, that it is by no means sufficient to show how the heat which falls upon Jupiter may be stored up, through the action of some component of his atmosphere in preventing its radiation into space. It is, indeed, of the utmost importance to know that even this is possible, because we are thus enabled to see that Jupiter is not necessarily an abode so bleak and desolate as some writers have imagined. In the following passage, Professor Tyndall has exhibited the means by which this result may be brought about, and the inhabitants of the noblest planet in the solar system placed somewhat higher in the scale of creation than Whewell surmised. "In these calculations," he remarked, referring to Whewell's estimate of the sun's heating power on Jupiter and the other exterior planets, "the influence of an atmospheric envelope was overlooked, and this omission vitiated the entire argument. It is perfectly possible to find an atmosphere which would act the part of a *barb* to the solar rays, permitting their entrance toward the planet, but preventing their withdrawal. For example, a layer of air, two inches in thickness, and saturated with the vapor of sulphuric ether, would offer very little resistance to the passage of the ether rays, but I find that it would cut off fully thirty-five per cent of the planetary radiation. It would require no inordinate thickening of the layer of vapor to double this absorption; and it is perfectly evident that, with a protecting envelope of this kind, permitting the heat to enter but preventing its escape, a comfortable temperature might be obtained on the surface of our most distant planet." The difference between such an arrangement as this and the way in which the earth's temperature is obtained, is the exact converse of that dealt with when we were considering the case of Mercury and Venus. Precisely as the mean temperature of the atmosphere of either of the interior planets may be no higher than that of our own air, while yet the sun's direct rays continue wholly unbearable, so the outer planets may have a perfectly comfortable temperature, while yet that direct solar heat which exerts so many important influences on the earth must be supplied only in quantities which we should find wholly inadequate for our wants.

I am far from desiring to infer that Jupiter must therefore be uninhabited, or even that the creatures existing on his surface must necessarily differ wholly in their nature from any with which we are familiar. But I think that, while, on the one hand, we must reject one of the chief arguments by which Whewell was led to people Jupiter with cartilaginous and glutinous creatures (!) floating in boundless oceans, so, on the other, we cannot accept without question the argument by which an effort has been made to indicate the possibility of a close correspondence between Jupiter's climate and our earth's.

And here we are led to the most interesting and suggestive of all the relations exhibited by Jupiter, or rather to three closely-associated relations, which lead to views of a somewhat startling character.

In common with the other large planets lying outside the zone of the asteroids, Jupiter has a mean density falling very far short of the mean density of the earth or the other small planets which travel within that zone. According to the best estimates of his mass and apparent diameter, his mean density would seem to be rather less than one-fourth of the earth's, or greater than the density of water by about one-third. It is worthy of remark, in fact, that his density is almost exactly the same as the sun's, and considerably greater than that of the other three outer planets hitherto discovered.

If we were quite certain that the disk measured by us exhibits the real outline of the planet, or that his atmosphere was not of abnormal extent, and that his globe was solid throughout, it would follow that the substances composing Jupiter were either altogether different from those forming our earth, or that they were combined in very different proportions. On the last point we can form no opinion. On the first we must be guided by the appearance of the planet.

Thus we are led to the second of the three relations just mentioned—the appearance of well-marked but variable belts on the planet—and of other indications implying the existence of an atmosphere of great extent.

The belts of Jupiter are commonly arranged with a certain symmetry on either side of the great equatorial bright belt, but sometimes there is a rather marked contrast between the northern and the southern halves of the planet. In color the dark belts are usually—when seen with suitable telescopic power[1]—of a coppery, ruddy, or even purplish tint, while the intermediate light bands vary from a pearly white in the equatorial belt, through yellowish white in the middle latitudes of both hemi-

---

[1] What is required is not so much a high light-gathering as a high magnifying power, though both points are of importance. When the light is not adequately reduced by increase of magnifying power, the color is lost in the resulting "glare." Reflectors seem to have an advantage over refractors in exhibiting the colors of the planets; at least, nearly all the accounts in which the appearance of color has been specially dwelt upon have been received from observers who have used reflectors.

spheres, to a grayish or even bluish tint at the poles.

There is every reason to believe that these belts indicate the existence of a very extensive vapor-laden atmosphere. The dark belts must not be considered as the true cloud-belts, because it must be remembered that we look upon the reverse side of the skyscape presented during the day to the Jovials: so that where they see densely-compacted dark clouds, we see the light which those clouds have intercepted; and, on the other hand, where they see clear spaces, the light which reaches them is not reflected to us without a considerable loss of brilliancy. Thus the dark belts of Jupiter are those regions where—if at all—we see the true surface of the planet.

Now, viewing the belts in this light, have we any means of judging from their aspect what is the extent of the planet's atmosphere? So far as I know, the question has never been considered, but it is well worthy of careful study.

It seems clear, in the first place, that if the bright belts really are cloud-belts, and the dark belts the surface of the planet, then on the edge of the planet's disk we ought to see some irregularity of level —the cloud-belts projecting slightly beyond the real outline of the planet—if the atmosphere have that enormous extent which some astronomers have supposed. Whether such an appearance has ever been looked for I do not know, but it has certainly never yet been detected.

We are forced to conclude, then, that either the atmosphere of Jupiter is not sufficiently extensive to interfere appreciably with our measurement of the planet's bulk, or else the dark belts belong but to a lower cloud-layer, not to the planet's real surface.

We have further evidence on this point in the appearance of dark spots on the dusky belts. These spots have even been described as black, though surely their appearing of that hue must be ascribed to the effect of contrast. Now, these dark spots, which have been seen by Cassini, Mädler, Schwabe, Airy, and others, may be regarded as the real surface of the planet (unless they belong to a yet deeper cloud-layer), seen for a while through openings in the cloud-bed to which the dusky belts belong. The reader will not fail to notice here some resemblance to what has been already mentioned respecting the sun-spots; and when we come to the third and most striking of the associated features I am now dealing with, it will be seen that there may be more in the analogy than one might at first sight be disposed to imagine.

How far the appearance of small round white spots on the dark belts may be considered as indicative of the extent and constitution of the Jovial atmosphere, it is not very easy to determine. That they are dense clouds, hanging suspended above the dusky cloud-layer, must be admitted as highly probable, but it is open to question whether they have formed there in the same way that cirrus-clouds are seen to form at a great elevation above a layer of cumulus-clouds, or whether they indicate the action of volcanoes beneath the dusky layer, propelling enormous streams of vapor through the superincumbent cloud-beds.

The third point on which I have to dwell is the variability of the belt-system, under which head I include not only variations in shape and extent, but those much more significant changes of color which have been recently discovered.

So far as is yet known, there is no recognizable law in the changes of shape exhibited by the belts of Jupiter—no periodicity or intelligible sequence. It may be suggested, in passing, that a systematic and persistent scrutiny of the planet might lead to the discovery of laws of this sort, which could not fail to indicate physical conclusions of the utmost importance. Nay, further, since we cannot doubt that the condition of the real surface of Jupiter is in some sort reflected, so to speak, in the aspect of his cloud-envelopes, it seems far from unlikely that a scrutiny of this sort might tell us where his oceans and continents, where his deserts, lakes, or rivers, are situated, even though no direct evidence of their existence might ever reward the observer. In these days, however, nine-tenths of those who are fortunate enough to possess fine telescopes prefer either to leave them idle, or to employ their powers in making observations, at great pains and labor, which are not worth the paper on which they are recorded.[1]

---

[1] It is painful to those who know what might be done in the numerous fine observatories now existing throughout England, to see the powers of

The few original observers we have are overtasked by the multitude of questions of interest presented to their consideration, so that many subjects of inquiry must perforce wait, either till their turn arrives, or till those who have the means of studying them choose to turn their thoughts from the sterile subjects they are now engaged upon.

So far, then, as inquiries have as yet been pushed, all that can be asserted on the subject we are considering is, that the planet's belts vary greatly in form, extent, and general appearance. At one time the dusky belts cover a large proportion of the planet's disk, at another they are singularly narrow. Now they are very regularly disposed, now they seem in some way under the action of disturbing forces of great intensity, causing them to assume the most irregular figure. The accompanying picture of the planet (Fig. 1) as seen by Mr. Browning, with

---

many noble instruments—the *chef-d'œuvres* of English and Continental opticians—devoted to puny imitations of the work done at Greenwich and other similar establishments. I speak on the authority of one of the first, if not the very first, of our professional astronomers, when I say that these imitations, even though they approached in character—which they do not and cannot—the operations superintended so ably by the Astronomer Royal, would be a simple waste of time and labor. Nor is this the only way in which fine telescopes are wasted. While on every side there are subjects of research which most pressingly require investigation, many of those who possess the requisite means and leisure for the purpose—nay, are not wanting in the necessary taste for observational research—are unhappily applying themselves to going over, perhaps with relatively inferior powers, ground which has already been thoroughly ransacked by our great observers. With some ten or twelve exceptions—which it is unnecessary to name—our private observatories seem to have banished everything resembling originality.

one of his own reflectors, indicates an appearance not
uncommonly seen, a dark streak extending obliquely
across the planet's equatorial regions. The number
of belts is singularly variable. Sometimes only one
has been seen, at others there have been as many as
five or six on each side of the planet's equator. In

FIG. 1.—The Planet Jupiter (Browning).

the course of a single hour, Cassini saw a complete
new belt form on the planet, and on December 13,
1690, two well-marked belts vanished completely,
while a third had almost disappeared in the same
short interval of time.

But if we seem to recognize here the action of
forces much more intense than those which influence
the condition of the earth's atmosphere, we have still

more striking evidence to the same purpose in the changes of color which have recently been detected in the great equatorial belt. This belt is usually of a pearly white tint, and has long been recognized as one of the most constant features of the planet's aspect. As the mean surface of this belt cannot be less than a fifth of the whole surface of the planet, it is clear that any changes which may take place in its general aspect cannot but be of the utmost significance. Now, during the autumn of 1869 and the spring of 1870, this belt has been more strongly colored than any part of the planet. Mr. Browning, observing Jupiter in the earlier part of the above-named interval, found the equatorial belt of a green-ish-yellow color, which deepened in October, 1869, to a full ochreish yellow, and in January of the present year had assumed an even darker tint, resembling yellow ochre. On one occasion, and on one only, he detected this tint in the first bright belt north of the equator. While thus exhibiting strongly-marked and changing colors, the equatorial belt has lost its right to be called, *par excellence*, the bright belt of the planet, being considerably inferior in brilliancy to the narrow bright belts north and south of it.

Other observers have also seen these colors. Mr. Slack, with a 6-inch Browning-With reflector, and Mr. Brindley, with an $8\frac{1}{2}$-inch telescope of the same construction, have witnessed most of the changes of color above described; and I myself, using Mr. Browning's $12\frac{1}{4}$-inch telescope, found the greenish-yellow tint of the equatorial belt last autumn altogether unmistakable.[1]

In the phenomena here described we have a problem whose interpretation is far from easy. Changes in the shape, disposition, and extent of the dark belts are sufficiently intelligible when we associate them, as we seem justified in doing, with variations in the position of the currents which traverse the vaporous envelope of Jupiter as the trades and counter-trades traverse the earth's atmosphere. But the equatorial zone is Jupiter's belt of calms, resembling in this respect the equatorial region, called by sailors the "doldrums," and, though occasional storms might be expected to agitate this region, yet processes of change, continuing for several months in succession, can evidently not be attributed to any such cause. We are taught, by the progress of recent research, to regard the color of the light derived from any source as a relation of the most instructive character, and changes of color, especially changes affecting so enormous a body as Jupiter, and so extensive a proportion of his surface, cannot but be looked upon as highly significant. Supposing we regard the ordinarily white light of the equatorial belt as indicative of the existence of enormous

---

[1] I had written thus far only, when I attended the meeting of the Royal Astronomical Society on January 14, 1870, where Mr. Buckingham, the owner of the great refractor, $21\frac{1}{4}$ inches in aperture, from whose performance so much was expected, mentioned that, as seen with this powerful instrument, the great belt was resolved into a number of small colored clouds on a white ground.

masses of cloud reflecting ordinary solar light to us, then we should have to regard the appearance of any other color over this region as an indication that these cloud-masses had been, through some unknown cause, either wholly or in part swept away. But— passing over the objection that this view leaves our difficulty unexplained—even if we assumed that in this way a portion of the surface of Jupiter had been brought into view, wholly or partially, why should this surface not exhibit a constant appearance? We cannot suppose changes affecting Jupiter's real sur- face are taking place with sufficient rapidity to ex- plain the series of strange color-changes observed by Messrs. Browning, Slack, and other astronomers. But if, on the other hand, we assume that a portion of the light ordinarily received from the bright belt is inherent—that is, that the planet is, to some ex- tent, self-luminous—then there remains the difficulty of explaining by what conceivable processes the equatorial regions are filled with a yellow light, so full and bright as to reach our earth from beyond four hundred millions of miles.

But I have spoken of the three relations last con- sidered—the small density of Jupiter, his extensive atmosphere, and the changes which take place in the shape and color of his belts—as associated phenomena. It remains that I should endeavor to justify this state- ment.

We know that Whewell, reasoning from the low specific gravity of Jupiter, was led to the conclusion that either the substance of the planet is wholly watery, or else a few cinders in the centre of Jupiter's globe constitute the only solid portion of his substance. It need hardly be said that the whole progress of modern astronomy is opposed to this view. We have seen that in the sun the same elements exist as in the earth, and that in the only planet whose nature we have been able to examine satisfactorily we find evidence of the existence of the same forms of matter that we see around us. It cannot but be held as highly improbable that the earth is the only member of the planetary system whose substance thus closely resembles that of the parent orb, nor is it likely that Mars is the only planet whose general atmospheric constitution resembles the earth's. Far more probably the lesson we are really to learn from these circumstances is, that throughout the solar system a general similarity of constitution exists, the sun being, so to speak, the type of the family over which he rules. Differences of *condition* we are compelled to recognize, since the sun itself, though constituted of the same elements as the earth, is in so different a state and has a mean density relatively so small; but we have no evidence justifying us in believing that any important differences of constitution exist throughout the solar system.

Thus, we are led to regard the singularly small density of Jupiter, and of the other planets outside the orbits of the asteroids, as due rather to some peculiarity in the condition of these orbs than to any such peculiarity of structure as Whewell insisted on. It will be seen at once that Jupiter's ex-

tensive atmospheric envelope and the strange changes
in the aspect of his belts are circumstances which
tend strikingly to confirm this impression. Let it be
remembered that, supposing Jupiter's globe even to
be wholly covered with water, yet a sun twenty-five
times further off than ours could not by any possibility load his atmosphere with the enormous masses
of vapor actually present in it. Let it be remembered, further, that the relatively sluggish action of
the sun upon Jupiter could not by any possibility
give rise to atmospheric disturbances so tremendous
as those which are evidenced by the rapid changes
of figure of his cloud-bands.[1] When to this we add
the relative minuteness of the seasonal changes on
Jupiter, we see at once that, unless some other cause
than solar action were at work, the condition of Jupiter's atmosphere ought to be very much calmer than
that of the earth's.

It seems to me that these considerations point
with tolerable clearness to the conclusion that, within
the orb which presents so glorious an aspect upon
our skies, processes of disturbance must be at work

---

[1] It is worthy of consideration, also, that even though the sun acted
as efficiently upon the air and oceans of Jupiter (assumed to be similar
to our own), yet atmospheric disturbances (due chiefly, as we know, to
these two forms of action) could not possibly be so violent even as on
our own earth, since corresponding latitudes of Jupiter (that is, regions
where corresponding effects would be experienced) are separated by distances so very much greater. It is clear that, if along a certain zone of
a planet the sun exerts a certain amount of influence, while along another he exerts a different influence, the result of the difference, looked
on as a cause of atmospheric disturbance, must be smaller as the distance between the zones is greater.

wholly different from any taking place on our own earth. That enormous atmospheric envelope is loaded with vaporous masses by some influence exerted from beneath its level. Those disturbances which take place so frequently and so rapidly are the evidences of the action of forces enormously exceeding those which the sun can by any possibility exert upon so distant a globe. And if analogy is to be our guide, and we are to judge of the condition of Jupiter according to what we know or guess of the past condition of the earth and the present condition of the sun, we seem led to the conclusion that Jupiter is still a glowing mass, fluid probably throughout, still bubbling and seething with the intensity of the primeval fires, sending up continually enormous masses of cloud, to be gathered into bands under the influence of the swift rotation of the giant planet. No otherwise, as it seems to me, can one explain the intense vitality, if one may use the expression, of a planet circumstanced as Jupiter is. No otherwise can one understand whence his atmosphere is loaded with vapor-masses whose contents must exceed, on a moderate computation, all the oceans on the surface of this earth. When we see masses so enormous swayed by influences of such energy, that intermediate belts, thousands of miles in width, are closed up in a single hour;[1] when we recognize the tremendous character

---

[1] Even if we take the disappearance of a dark belt to be due to the formation of clouds, which is perhaps more probable than that the clouds of neighboring belts have *closed in*, the forces represented by the change are nevertheless tremendous.

of the motions which, from beyond four hundred millions of miles, are distinctly cognizable by our telescopes, we see that we have no ordinary phenomena to deal with, and that the theory we adopt for their explanation cannot be otherwise than striking and surprising.

If the view which I have here put forward—or rather, the view to which I have been led by a careful consideration of the phenomena which Jupiter presents to our contemplation—be indeed correct, we must of course dismiss the idea that the giant planet is at present a fit abode for living creatures. Yet need we not turn from his system with the thought that here at least our hopes of recognizing other worlds have been disappointed. If Jupiter be still in a sense a sun, not indeed resplendent like the great centre of the planetary scheme, but still a source of heat, is there not excellent reason for believing that the system which circles around him consists of four worlds where life—even such forms of life as we are familiar with—may still exist? Those four orbs, which our telescopes reveal to us as tiny points of light, are in reality globes which may be compared with the four worlds that circle nearest to the sun. I have shown that they cannot subserve the purpose which many astronomers have ascribed to them, of compensating Jupiter for the small amount of light he receives, even if they could be seen from any point of his cloud-encompassed surface. So that, even adopting the commonplace and superficial view that the purpose of any object may

be regarded as ascertained when we have been able
to ask (without any obvious answer) what other purpose it *can* subserve, we still are led to the belief
that the satellites of Jupiter must be the abode of
life, since on this view, and on this view only, we
find a *raison d'être* both for the planet and for the
system which circles around him.

There are no considerations which appear directly
opposed to the view that Jupiter is in a sense a
sun. It need hardly be said that I do not regard
him as being in the same condition as the central
luminary of the planetary system. He is not an
incandescent body, or, if he is, the greater part of
his light is veiled by the cloud-envelopes which surround him. The solar clouds are, as we know, themselves luminous; those of Jupiter are not so, a circumstance which indicates that the heat of Jupiter
is not sufficient to vaporize those substances which
are incandescent when in the liquid state. The
outer layer of clouds must, therefore, be regarded as
for the most part aqueous. We see *there*, in fact,
the future oceans of Jupiter, if the hypothesis I am
now dealing with be correct.

That Jupiter may supply an immense amount of
heat to his satellites (on this view of his condition)
is perfectly clear, since the amount of light he emits
is no adequate measure of the amount of obscure
heat which radiates from him to the four worlds
around him. When we consider the enormous apparent size of Jupiter as seen from his satellites, we
recognize at once how large a supply of heat he is

capable of transmitting to them. From the outermost satellite his apparent diameter exceeds that of the sun (as seen by us) some eightfold, and his apparent size, therefore, exceeds the sun's more than sixty-fold. From the innermost he is seen with a diameter nearly forty times that of the sun, and with an apparent area more than fourteen hundred times as large as his.

We have evidence, however, which renders it far from improbable that Jupiter may emit some small proportion of light. I have already referred to the singular excess of his brilliancy over that due to his size and his distance from the sun and from us. The estimates of Zöllner, the eminent photometrician, serve to show, not, indeed, that Jupiter sends more light to us than he receives from the sun, but that he sends much more light than a planet of equal size and constituted like Mars, the moon, or the earth, could possibly reflect to us if placed where Jupiter is. Whereas Mars reflects but one-fourth of the light he receives, Jupiter reflects more than three-fifths. The moon sends less than a fifth; Saturn, Jupiter's brother giant, more than a half. The late Professor G. Bond, of America, actually calculated that Jupiter sends forth more light than he receives. Whether his observations or the more systematic observations of the German astronomer are accepted, we see that, unless we adopt some such hypothesis as I have dealt with above, we must recognize a marked difference between the relative light-reflecting capacities of the two largest planets of the system, and those of Mars or the moon. In fact, from other researches of Dr. Zöllner's it follows that, if Jupiter does not shine in part by native light, his surface must possess reflective powers nearly equal to those of white paper. Now, this would scarcely be credible, even though under the telescope the planet's surface were found to be universally white; but, as we find a large proportion of it to be of a dull coppery hue, we seem forced to admit that it cannot really have an average reflective power nearly so great as that calculated by Zöllner. It follows, as at least highly probable, that Jupiter shines in part by his own light, and this being admitted, we cannot but regard it as highly probable that the mass of the planet must be intensely hot.

It may seem, at first sight, that the apparent blackness of the satellites' shadows, as seen on the disk of Jupiter, is wholly opposed to the view that any portion of his light is native. But, as a matter of fact, there is no force at all in this consideration, or rather, whatever weight we may attach to the observed appearance of the satellites' shadows is in favor of the strange theory here put forward. For it has been a subject of remark among the most experienced observers, that a satellite in transit will occasionally appear as dark as its shadow, both seeming black. The blackness, then, is only apparent, and an effect of contrast. In reality, if such observations as I have mentioned are to be trusted (and I know no reason for disregarding them), the shadow of a satellite is not black, and therefore there seems no escape from the conclusion that the surface on which they are projected is partially self-luminous.

A stronger argument against the belief that Jupiter is self-luminous, lies in the fact that the satellites disappear in his shadow. It must be remembered, however, that in any case we can assign but a small proportion of inherent light to Jupiter, and that his satellites would, therefore, in any case, lose so large a proportion of their light when passing into his shadow, that we might expect them to disappear, even under the closest telescopic scrutiny.

Although I have already far exceeded the limits I had proposed to myself for the consideration of this noble planet, it is with regret that I take leave of him to pass onward to the outermost bounds of the solar system. I would fain dwell even longer than I have, on a subject of contemplation at once so interesting and so instructive. Jupiter, the centre of a noble system of worlds, or Jupiter, himself a world, inhabited by beings as high perhaps in the scale of creation as he himself is in the scheme of the planets, is alike a worthy subject of study. The more one dwells on the features he presents, the more one is impressed with the sense of the grandeur of his position in the universe. Surely, whether now inhabited or not, he *must* be intended to be one day the abode of noble races. Surely no astronomer worthy the name can regard this grand orb as the cinder-centred globe of watery matter so contemptuously dealt with by one who, be it remembered thankfully, was not an astronomer. He who has not

gazed hour after hour on the glories of the giant
planet, gathering fresh delight as feature after feature is revealed beneath his scrutiny—he who takes
his astronomy but at second-hand from the pages of
the real worker, turning from labors in other fields
"to see what these star-gazers have to say," may
lightly disregard the grand lesson which the heavens
are always teaching, and find only the grotesque and
the incongruous, where in reality there is the per-
fectest handiwork of the Creator.   But the astronomer, imbued with the sense of beauty and perfection which each fresh hour of world-study instils
more deeply into his soul, reads a nobler lesson in
the skies.   The music which reaches his ears may
be fitful, but it is not "as sweet bells jangled out of
tune and harsh"; he may not master its full meaning, though every note thrills through his inmost
soul; but, even when its sounds are least distinct,
they have a beauty and solemnity which are all their
own.   In fine, the true astronomer may say with the
Pythagorean, but in another sense:

> "There's not one orb which thou behold'st
> But in his motion like an angel sings,
> Still choiring to the young-eyed cherubim;
> But while this muddy vesture of decay
> Doth grossly close us in we cannot hear it."

CHAPTER VI

SATURN, THE RINGED WORLD

IF Jupiter by his commanding proportions affords a forceful argument against the view that our tiny earth is the only real world in the solar system, Saturn supplies an argument of scarcely inferior strength in the singularly complex character of the scheme of which he is the centre. No one can contemplate this glorious planet, as shown by a telescope of adequate power, without being impressed by the conviction that he is looking at a world altogether more important in the scheme of creation than the globe on which he lives. Whether he recognizes in the present condition of the planet the result of the action of those laws which the Almighty has assigned to His universe, or whether he prefers the view that Saturn and his system are seen now as they were fashioned at the beginning by the Almighty's creative hand, he is alike amazed at the wealth of design exhibited in the scene he is gazing upon. He may not be able, indeed, to appreciate the true character of the purposes which the various parts of the Saturnian system are intended to sub-

(165)

serve, or he may, in the rash attempt to solve the mighty problem, be led to erroneous conceptions; but that the great planet *is* designed for purposes of the noblest sort, he cannot gravely question.[1]

In volume and mass Saturn is inferior to Jupiter. Jupiter is twelve hundred and thirty times, Saturn is not quite seven hundred times, as large as the earth; and, while Jupiter outweighs her three hundred times, Saturn is scarcely ninety times as heavy as she is. Still Saturn is sufficiently large and massive to dwarf our earth to insignificance; and even Uranus and Neptune, though belonging to the family of the major planets, and giants compared with the earth, fall below Saturn far more than he does below Jupiter. Like Jupiter, Saturn rotates very rapidly on his axis, the length of his day being about 10½ of our hours. The materials of which Saturn is composed have a mean density not much greater than half that of Jupiter, or less than three-fourths of the mean density of water. In fact, Saturn's substance is specifically lighter than that of any known planet. It seems not impossible that we have in this relation some indication of the true cause of that complexity of detail which the Saturnian system exhibits.

The equator of Saturn is inclined about 28¼ degrees to the plane in which the planet moves, so that

---

[1] I know nothing better calculated to lead men to choose astronomy as their favorite subject of study than the contemplation of the Saturnian system. I can well remember the sensations with which—some eight years since—I saw the ringed planet for the first time. I look on that view as my introduction to the most fascinating of all the sciences.

his seasons (so far as they depend on this circumstance) closely resemble in character those of the planet Mars. He occupies about 29½ years in circling once round the sun—this therefore is the length of the Saturnian year. His distance from the sun is nearly twice that of Jupiter, and nearly ten times that of the earth; so that the amount of light and heat which any portion of his surface receives from the sun is about ₉₁st part of that received by a similar portion of the earth's. His orbit being somewhat eccentric, however, there is a considerable variation in this respect during the course of a Saturnian year, insomuch that when he is nearest to the sun he receives more light than when in aphelion in the proportion of about five to four.

Most of the relations which have to be considered in discussing the habitability of Saturn have been already dealt with (under very similar conditions) in treating of other planets; so that I propose to touch on them very lightly, in order to come more quickly to those circumstances which distinguish Saturn specially among the other members of the solar system.

Gravity at his equator is almost exactly equal to gravity at the earth's surface. Near the poles there is a marked increase in the action of Saturnian gravity, insomuch that a body weighing ten pounds at his equator would weigh about twelve pounds at either pole. There is nothing, however, in this peculiarity which need be specially dwelt upon.

The length of the Saturnian year, and the small quantity of light and heat received from the sun, are

simply more marked instances of what has already
been considered in the case of Jupiter. We may
conclude with some confidence that these relations
are quite sufficient to render Saturn wholly uninhabitable by such creatures as exist upon the earth; but
there seems no reason for supposing that (so far as
these relations alone are concerned) the planet may
not be the abode of living beings as high in the scale
of creation as any which live upon our globe.

And thus viewing Saturn, we cannot regard even
the exceptional effects produced by his ring-system
as of themselves sufficient to banish life from his surface. These effects are not without interest, however,
and, as they have been made the subject of some discussion, I may be permitted to make a few remarks
upon them.

I apprehend that, when Sir John Herschel said
that the rings occasion an eclipse of nearly fifteen
years in duration, first to the northern and then to
the southern hemisphere of the planet, he meant
simply that during an interval of such length a large
portion of either hemisphere was in shadow. He
knew perfectly well that, long after the edge of the
ring has been turned directly toward the sun, a very
large proportion of the hemisphere, over which the
ring's shadow proceeds to sweep, remains illuminated.
It had always seemed to me, therefore, altogether a
mistake on the part of Dr. Lardner to interpret Herschel's words as though implying that a whole hemisphere of the planet is eclipsed for fifteen years in
succession.

So misinterpreting the expression used by Sir John Herschel, Dr. Lardner, in his desire to show that no such relation existed, was led into real mistakes which a sounder mathematician would not have fallen into. He examined the relations presented by the ring in a *quasi*-mathematical, but inexact, manner, and came to the following conclusions: "That, by the apparent motions of the heavens produced by the diurnal rotation of Saturn, the celestial objects, including the sun and the eight satellites, are not carried parallel to the edges of the rings; that they are moved so as to pass alternately from side to side of these edges; that, in general, such objects as pass under the rings are only occulted by them for short intervals before and after their meridional culmination (*sic*); that, although, under some rare and exceptional circumstances and conditions, certain objects —the sun being among the number—are occulted from rising to setting, the endurance of these phenomena is not such as has been supposed, and the places of their occurrence are far more limited." All these statements are more or less incorrect, and most of them are the direct reverse of the truth. The seven inner satellites of Saturn stand in an altogether different relation, with respect to the rings, than all other celestial objects, since they travel in the same plane and in circles concentric with the outlines of the rings: they can, therefore, no more be occulted by the rings than an outer ring can be occulted by an inner one. So far is it again from being true that the sun is in general only occulted for a short time before and after culmination, that the more common case (considering the whole planet) is for the sun to be eclipsed (if at all) throughout the whole of the Saturnian day; and a very common case, left altogether unnoticed by Dr. Lardner, is, that the sun is occulted in the forenoon and afternoon, but free from eclipse in the middle of the day. Nor is it true that the places where the sun can be totally eclipsed throughout the day are limited to a relatively small portion of the planet, since every part of the planet whence the rings are visible at all has the sun eclipsed by the rings throughout the whole day for a longer or shorter succession of rotations, and, in the remaining or polar regions of the planet, the sun is altogether absent for long intervals of time, for the same reason that he is absent from the skies of our polar regions during a comparatively short interval. As for the endurance of the total diurnal eclipses, it is only necessary to remark that, in Saturnian latitudes corresponding to that of London or Paris, the sun is totally eclipsed for more than five years in succession, while in a latitude corresponding to that of Madrid he is totally eclipsed for nearly seven years in succession. This suffices to show that an arrangement which the inhabitants of the earth would find wholly unendurable prevails over a very large proportion of Saturn's surface.[1]

---

[1] The views here expressed as to the effects of the Saturnian rings are founded on exact mathematical calculation, of which the elements are given in my treatise on Saturn. The problem is not by any means a difficult one, and the only way in which the erroneous views formed

But, if we consider the matter rightly, we shall see that this, after all, need not surprise us, since there is already in the enormous distance of Saturn from the sun the amplest reason for believing that he cannot be inhabited by such creatures as exist upon the earth. It is in vain that, by conceiving him to be surrounded by a dense atmosphere, we assign to him a mean climate as warm as that of the earth. The want of direct solar heat still remains, and must be regarded as a fatal objection to the habitability of Saturn by races resembling those with which we are familiar.

In the case of Saturn as in the case of Jupiter, the provision of satellites, and of the rings which form so glorious an object to the astronomer on earth, is altogether inadequate to increase the supply of light received by the Saturnians to any such extent as has been imagined. Those well-meaning persons who insist on their own interpretation of the Almighty's designs, are singularly successful in overlooking very obvious difficulties. If the design of the rings, for instance, really were to compensate the Saturnians for the small amount of light which they receive from the sun, it would surely follow that there was a want of wisdom in the selection of an arrangement by which

by Dr. Lardner can be explained is, by considering that he dealt with the problem in a general instead of an exact manner. I could not feel any doubt as to the accuracy of my results, but I was not the less pleased to receive a letter from Mr. Freeman, a Fellow of St. John's College, Cambridge, stating that he had obtained similar results, and had constructed a table on the plan of Table XI. in my "Saturn," and so closely according with it as not to need separate publication.

more light is kept away from Saturn than the rings can possibly reflect to him. And further, during the very season when the extra light derived from the rings is most required by the planet, that is, during the long nights of the Saturnian winter, they exhibit a dark band upon the heavens, concealing whole constellations from the view of the Saturnian people. As far as the satellites are concerned, there is no corresponding difficulty. They undoubtedly reflect the sun's light to Saturn, and, if there really are intelligent beings on the planet, the satellites must undoubtedly present an interesting spectacle, especially when a large number of the moons are nearly full. But a little consideration will show that, even though all the satellites were full at the same time, the quantity of light they could send back to their primary would be wholly inadequate to compensate for the planet's great distance from the sun. According to the best estimates of their magnitude, the eight satellites, taken in their order from the planet, cover spaces on the Saturnian heavens which bear to the space covered by our moon the respective proportions of about 2, 1, $1\frac{1}{4}$, $\frac{3}{4}$, $\frac{5}{8}$, $\frac{1}{3}$, $\frac{1}{100}$, $\frac{1}{70}$. In all, then, they cover an area about six times that of our moon; and as, owing to their great distance from the sun, they are illumined by only $\frac{1}{100}$th of the light which illuminates our moon, they could only send back to the planet, if it were possible for them to be all full together, about $\frac{1}{16}$th part of the light we receive from the full moon. It will be remembered that the light which could be reflected from the Jovial moons, if they could be all full together, bears about the same proportion to our moon's. We seem forced to the conclusion that the satellites were intended to subserve no such design as has been imagined. Here, as in many other cases, the scheme of the Creator is not so obvious to human reasoning as some have complacently supposed.

But we have now to consider peculiarities which suggest that Saturn's globe has not yet reached a condition fitting it to be the abode of living creatures. These peculiarities resemble in great part those which have been already noticed in the case of Jupiter, but a certain most remarkable phenomenon belongs to the ringed planet alone.

The belts of Saturn resemble those of Jupiter in their general shape and also in their color. The dark belts near the equator are of a faint brown or ruddy tinge, those near the pole bluish or greenish gray, while the bright belts are yellowish—the equatorial belt being the brightest of all and almost white. The poles are commonly dusky and even sombre in hue.

The belts change in aspect much as those of Jupiter have been observed to do; and whether we regard the change as due to the bodily transference of the belts of cloud or to the precipitation of their material in the form of rain (while, elsewhere, invisible vapors are condensed into cloud), we are compelled to recognize the action of forces altogether exceeding those which the sun can be supposed to exert upon this distant planet. The light sent to us from Saturn also bears a much greater proportion to the amount of solar light actually received by the planet than is observed in the case of Mars or the moon, and so nearly approaches the proportion noticed in the case of Jupiter as to lead to the same inference—namely, that a portion of Saturn's light is emitted from the body of the planet.

In these respects, and also in the small density of the planet, we seem to recognize evidence which points to Saturn as probably a heat-sun (if not to any very noteworthy extent a light-sun) to the satellites which circle around him, and not himself the abode of living creatures. Without dwelling further on evidence already fully considered in the case of Jupiter, I turn to one of the most striking facts in the whole range of observational astronomy, as supplying at once new evidence respecting the condition of Saturn and strengthening the evidence adduced respecting Jupiter.

If it can be shown that Saturn's globe is subject to changes of figure perceptible even across the enormous gap which separates him from the earth, it will at once be admitted that he can hardly be regarded as a globe conveniently habitable. Now, I have very little hesitation in saying that evidence of the most conclusive kind exists in favor of this strange mobility of figure. It will presently be seen that it is with the observations of no mere amateur astronomers that I have to deal in endeavoring to establish as a fact that which has commonly been spoken of as an illusion—the assumption by Saturn of his so-called "square-shouldered" figure.

It was in April, 1805, that Sir William Herschel first called attention to this peculiarity. The planet, which had always presented to him an elliptical figure, exhibited a strangely-distorted aspect. A well-marked flattening at the equator, accompanied by an equally well-marked flattening at the poles, gave the planet's globe an oblong figure (with rounded angles), the longest diameters having their extremities in Saturnian latitude 43° 20′—so exactly was the great astronomer able to indicate the nature of the deformity, owing to its well-marked character.

What view shall we form respecting an observation of so remarkable a character? Was the peculiarity due to telescopic distortion? Herschel observed it with several instruments, some seven, some ten, one twenty, and one forty feet in length. Was the phenomenon due to atmospheric disturbances? Such disturbances could not account for a persistent impression, however well they might explain the momentary assumption of the square-shouldered aspect by the ringed planet. Besides, Jupiter presented no such appearance. Was the appearance an optical illusion due to the position of the ring— then slightly open? If so, the planet should always exhibit the square-shouldered aspect when his rings are open to that particular extent; and this is not the case. Besides, we ought to notice a similar illusion, when looking at a picture representing that particular phase of Saturn. Must we, then, accept the astounding conclusion that the giant bulk of Saturn is subject to throes of so tremendous a nature as to upheave whole zones of his surface five or six hundred miles above their ordinary level? Truly the conclusion is one to be avoided, if we can by any possibility find a less startling explanation of the matter.

Yet where are we to look for such an explanation? Was Sir William Herschel simply deceived? I have already considered the general question of illusion, but the reader might entertain the explanation as conceivable that Herschel might for a while have lost the acumen which distinguished him—that illness, for example, might have rendered his observations inexact. But we have abundant evidence that the great astronomer was in the full possession of all his wonderful powers as an observer during the month of April, 1805; we know further that by careful measurements he rigidly excluded all possibility of illusion affecting his judgment.

It would be more satisfactory, doubtless, to the reader, however, to learn that other observers had noticed similar peculiarities, or peculiarities which, if not similar, were at least such as to prepare us to regard the globe of Saturn as liable to remarkable changes of figure. Fortunately, many such observations have been recorded. I take the following from one of an admirable series of papers on Saturn by Mr. Webb, in the "Intellectual Observer" for 1866.

On August 5, 1803, Schröter found Saturn not perfectly spheroidal in figure. Kitchener says that for a few months in the autumn of 1818 he saw Saturn of the figure described by Sir William Her-

schel, and that with two different achromatics. At
this time the ring must have appeared too narrow to
account for the appearance as due to illusion. On
one occasion the Astronomer Royal had a similar
view of Saturn. He remarks, also, that a person
unacquainted with Herschel's observation remarked
spontaneously on the flattened equator of the planet.
On another occasion, Mr. Airy noticed the exact
reverse, the planet seeming flattened instead of upheaved, in latitude 45°. In January, 1855, Coolidge,
using the splendid refractor of the Cambridge, U. S.,
Observatory, noticed that the greatest diameter of
the globe seemed inclined about 20° to the equatorial
diameter; but on the 9th the equatorial diameter
seemed the greatest; while on December 6th he says,
"I cannot persuade myself that it is an optical illusion which makes the maximum diameter of the ball
intersect the limb half way between the northern
edge of the equatorial belt and the inner ellipse of
the inner bright ring." All this time the rings
were nearly at their greatest opening, so that any
illusion should have been of an opposite character
to that observed when the rings were nearly closed.
In the report of the Greenwich Observatory for
1860–61, it is stated that "Saturn has *sometimes*
appeared to exhibit the square-shouldered aspect."
The eminent observers Bond, father and son, have
noticed similar peculiarities, using the great Merz refractor already referred to. Each of them noticed
a flattening of the north-polar regions of the planet
in the summer of 1848, when the ring was turned

edgewise toward us. On the other hand, the same observers noticed that in 1855–57, when the ring was most widely opened, the polar regions did not always seem projected furthest on the outer ring in a symmetrical manner, but four times on the left of the pole, once on the right, and once only, exactly opposite the pole. "The outline of this region also occasionally appeared irregularly flattened and distorted," an appearance not satisfactorily explained by the juxtaposition of the dark shadow of the planet on the ring.

Now, there can be no doubt whatever that the planet Saturn is not ordinarily distorted. In 1832, during the disappearance of the ring, Bessel carefully determined the figure of the planet's disk, and Main in 1848 (when the ring was again turned edgewise toward us) made similar measurements. Each of these trustworthy authorities came to the conclusion that the disk of Saturn did not, at the seasons when they respectively measured it, exhibit any distortion of figure such as Herschel had described.

We seem almost compelled, therefore, to accept the conclusion that the planet Saturn is subject to the influence of forces which either upheave portions of its surface from time to time, or cause vast masses of cloud to rise to an enormous height above the mean layer of Saturn's cloud-envelope. Whichever view we adopt, we cannot fail to recognize the fact that an intense heat must in all probability prevail in the great globe of Saturn; and doubtless the real mass of the planet must emit a brilliant light, though the cloud-strata surrounding him may prevent us from recognizing more than a minute proportion of his luminosity. In fact, according to this view, Saturn and Jupiter, unlike the sun, whose real substance emits a less intense light than the cloud-photosphere surrounding him, must have nuclei—solid or liquid—shining with an altogether more brilliant light than the cloud-envelopes of these planets seem actually to emit.

Why Saturn, rather than Jupiter, should exhibit these mysterious changes of figure, is readily explicable when we remember the near coincidence of the planes in which the Jovial satellites move with the orbital plane of their primary. There thus always results a close agreement between the zone on which the satellites exert their greatest disturbing influences, and that most influenced by the solar action. No such coincidence exists in the case of Saturn, whose satellites travel in a plane inclined nearly thirty degrees to that in which their primary travels. It is worthy of mention, however, that Schröter, an accurate and practiced observer, records that on certain occasions he thought he could detect partial flattenings of the disk of Jupiter (see also Preface).

I think the evidence in the case of Saturn favors, at least as strongly as that which has been adduced in the case of Jupiter, the belief that the giant planets outside the zone of asteroids are not themselves suitable abodes for living creatures, but are suns, supplementing the small amount of light, and yet more fully supplementing the small amount of heat, which the sun supplies to the satellites which circle around these orbs. Undoubtedly, if we are to judge according to the method which has been so often applied to such questions, if we are to ask ourselves according to what arrangement the central planets and the schemes circling around them seem most reasonably interpreted, we should at once adopt some such conclusion. For, by taking Jupiter and Saturn to be strictly analogous to our own earth, and their satellites to be subsidiary bodies, resembling our moon in this, that they subserve at present no other purpose but to illuminate the nocturnal skies and to sway the oceans of their primaries, we find ourselves perplexed by the consideration that a much simpler arrangement would have subserved these purposes much more completely. In the case of Saturn's satellites, indeed, it seems difficult to conceive that these bodies could have been intended to fulfil any such purposes, since the two outer ones could neither give any useful light to their primary, nor sway appreciably any oceans which may exist upon the planet.

On the other hand, if Saturn and Jupiter are suns to their satellites, we see in the Saturnian and Jovial systems real miniatures of the solar system. We no longer require that the planets themselves should be habitable, any more than we require that our sun should be so. In fine, we do not find in any portion of either system that waste of material which perplexes us under the former arrangement.

I do not say that this mode of reasoning has any

great force.   On the contrary, I am disposed to
demur to the opinion that it is given to man to assign a reason for all things which science may reveal
to him.   For reasons which seem to me far more convincing, I am led, however, to believe that the two
most important members of the planetary scheme
must be left without inhabitants for the present,
while in exchange I submit to the contemplation of
the curious twelve small orbs, constituting two mini-
ature world-systems.   The condition of these worlds
will be touched on briefly in a separate chapter.

CHAPTER VII

URANUS AND NEPTUNE, THE ARCTIC PLANETS

A CIRCUMSTANCE which is of great importance in considering the relations of the outer planets is apt to be lost sight of, owing to the unsatisfactory manner in which, in nearly all books on astronomy, the planetary orbits are represented. To look at the series of equi-distant and concentric circles representing the orbits of the planets, who would suppose that, in passing from the orbit of Jupiter to that of Saturn, a distance five times as great as that which separates our earth from the sun has to be traversed? But the distance separating Uranus from Saturn is twice as great even as this tremendous gap, while Neptune travels as far beyond Uranus as Uranus beyond Saturn. Nine hundred millions of miles in width is the enormous gap by which the path of Uranus is separated from that of the ringed planet on the inner side, and from that of distant Neptune on the outer, so that a line equal to the diameter of Jupiter's orbit would barely suffice to reach from Saturn to Uranus, or from Uranus to Neptune, even when either pair of planets are in conjunction.

(182)

We know so little of the physical aspect of Uranus and Neptune that it is extremely difficult to form any opinion as to their condition. The two planets resemble each other in size, each being far smaller than either of the giant orbs we have lately been considering. Uranus has a diameter of about 33,250 miles; Neptune is somewhat larger, his diameter having been estimated at 37,250 miles. The volume of Uranus is 74, the volume of Neptune 105, times that of the earth. Both planets exceed Saturn in density; for, whereas Saturn's mean specific gravity is but $\frac{13}{100}$ths, that of Uranus is $\frac{18}{100}$ths, and that of Neptune $\frac{14}{100}$ths, of the mean specific gravity of our globe. Thus each planet has a density nearly equal to that of water. The mass of Uranus exceeds the earth's about $12\frac{1}{2}$ times, while that of Neptune is some $16\frac{3}{4}$ times as great as the earth's. It will be seen, therefore, that though these two far-distant worlds are much less massive than Jupiter or Saturn, each of them outweighs many times the combined mass of the four planets which travel within the zone of asteroids. Yet gravity on the surface of these two orbs is but about three-fourths of terrestrial gravity.

The disk of the sun as seen from Uranus is less that that which we see in the proportion of nearly 390 to 1, while the Neptunians have a sun only about $\frac{1}{900}$th of ours, in apparent size; and in these proportions the solar light and heat received by these planets are respectively diminished. So small does the sun appear, in fact, that to eyes such as ours his orb could not present a disk-like figure, but would appear like an exceedingly brilliant day-star.

So far we have found the circumstances of the two planets somewhat similar. But we have now to consider a relation presented by Uranus, which is not shared in by Neptune. It may be remarked that we know so little about either planet that any very careful consideration of their habitability would be simply a waste of labor. The evidence I am about to adduce, however, in the case of Uranus, seems thoroughly to dispose of the claim of this planet to be regarded as a world inhabited by creatures resembling those we are acquainted with on earth; and, as we cannot reasonably suppose Neptune to be inhabited by such creatures while Uranus is not, we may very fairly regard the question as disposed of for both planets, even though the relation dealt with is peculiar to Uranus.

We know that in the case of Jupiter, as in that of Saturn, the position of the plane near which the satellites travel is nearly coincident with the plane of the primary's equator. Therefore, though no telescope has yet exhibited any features on the disk of Uranus which can enable us to determine the position of its equator, we can reasonably infer from the motion of the satellites how the equator of the planet is situated.

Now, the satellites of Uranus travel in a plane very nearly at right angles to the plane in which the planet travels. It may be mentioned also, though not important for my present purpose, that they travel in

a retrograde direction. We conclude, then, that the
axis of Uranus lies very nearly in the plane wherein
the planet moves around the sun, and that the planet
rotates in such a way around this axis that the sun
moves across the Uranian skies from west to east,
instead of from east to west. The latter relation is
of no great importance; the former, however, involves results which dispose at once, and thoroughly,
of any hopes we might entertain of discovering creatures in Uranus resembling those which inhabit the
earth.

The inclination of the plane of Uranus's equator
to the path in which he travels being about 76 degrees, it follows that the Uranian sun has a range
of about 76 degrees on either side of the celestial
equator, during the long Uranian year. Already, in
considering the seasons of Venus, I have dealt with a
peculiarity of this sort; but in the case of Uranus the
effects are more serious. We have only to consider
what would be the result of so wide a range of solar
excursion north and south of the celestial equator in
a latitude corresponding to that of London, to see how
importantly the climatic relations of a planet like
Uranus, occupying eighty-four years in circling once
around the sun, must be affected by such a peculiarity. We know that in the latitude of London the
sun reaches at noon, in spring or autumn, an elevation of about $38\frac{1}{2}$ degrees above the southern horizon, that in summer he passes the meridian $23\frac{1}{2}$
degrees higher, while in winter he passes the meridian $23\frac{1}{2}$ degrees lower, or only fifteen degrees

above the horizon.   But in a similar Uranian latitude, while the sun would reach the same meridian
elevation in spring or autumn, he would in summer
travel throughout the day in a small circle, fourteen
degrees only from the pole (raised of course 51½ degrees above the northern horizon).   And obviously,
since the year of the Uranians lasts eighty-four of
our years, the continuance of the sun above the horizon would last for many years.[1]   So far there is
nothing to render life in Uranus unpleasant, always
supposing the small amount of light and heat supplied by the sun to be compensated by some such
atmospheric arrangements as physicists have thought
necessary for the convenience of the more distant
planets.   But, when we consider the nature of the
Uranian winter, we find the circumstances such as no
such arrangements can be conceived to alleviate.   The
winter path of the Uranian sun, in a latitude corresponding to that of London, is just as fully pressed
below the horizon as the summer path is raised above
it.   At midnight the sun is 65½ degrees, at nominal
noon he is 37½ degrees, below the southern horizon.
And as with the summer day, so with the winter
night, years elapse before either comes to an end.
For upward of twenty years, in a latitude corre-

---

[1] Exact calculation applied to relations so uncertain as those here in
question would be out of place.   From a careful construction, however,
with 76° as the assumed value of the inclination of the equator of
Uranus to the plane of his orbit, I find that the sun would continue
above his horizon in summer for about 23¼ years.   Of course, it follows that the sun would continue below the horizon for an equally long
period in winter!

sponding to that of London, the Uranians—if there are any—never see the small Uranian sun. During all this long time, too, a sight even is denied them of all parts of the solar system, interior to the orbit of Uranus; though this deprivation cannot be regarded as very serious when it is remembered that to such eyesight as ours Saturn could barely be visible from Uranus, even when most favorably situated,[1] while Jupiter, always near the sun, could only be occasionally seen, shining with a light somewhat less than a fiftieth of that which he reflects to us when in opposition.

When we consider other latitudes, we still find Uranus ill provided for as respects his winter season. In all latitudes nearer the pole than the latitude just considered, the Uranians have winters lasting from twenty years to upward of forty. In latitudes nearer the equator the winter night is shorter, but we must approach quite close to the equator before we reach a latitude where the winter night lasts less than a year or so. Over a belt extending about fourteen degrees on each side of the equator there is a perennial succession of days and nights never exceeding the full duration of the Uranian diurnal rotation.

---

[1] Admiral Smyth speaks of Saturn as a fine morning and evening star for the Uranians; but, though Saturn may be visible, he can hardly be a fine object. At his elongations he is twice as far from the Uranians as he is from us when in opposition, and further he presents but a half disk. His light must in fact be reduced to less than one-eighth of that which he presents to us when in opposition; and, as, instead of being on a black sky, he must be always seen from Uranus on a twilight sky, he cannot appear a very fine object.

But we must not suppose that we have thus found an Elysian zone in Uranus. The immense range of the sun's excursions produces here also a variety of seasonal changes which we should find altogether unendurable. From a sun barely rising above the horizon in winter, to a sun which rises vertically overhead twice in the course of the Uranian summer, is a change which hardly accords with our views of what is desirable in the progress of the seasons. At the equator itself there are in reality two summers, occurring at the period of the sun's passing the celestial equator. Here for many years together the sun passes day after day to a point nearly overhead. But then comes the long winter, in the heart of which the sun rises barely fourteen degrees above the northern or southern horizon. By whatever arrangement we render the long Uranian winters in this part of the planet endurable, we render the heat of his long summers unendurable; and *vice versa,* if we conceive of atmospheric relations which would render his summers pleasing, we have caused his winters to be so intensely cold that no creatures we are familiar with could endure the prolonged and bitter frosts, contrasting so distressingly with the imagined geniality of his summer weather.

If Uranus be inhabited at all, then, it must be by creatures constituted in a very different manner from any with which we are acquainted. To such creatures, if any among them be gifted with intelligence, the heavens, though not adorned with planets, must yet present an interesting subject of study.

The position of the pole, lying close by the zodiac, so that among the zodiacal constellations there must be all the varieties of motion which we recognize in passing from the equatorial to polar constellations, would lead to a certain complexity in celestial charts and globes, which would invite us to the conclusion that the Uranians must be capital mathematicians. Then there are certain astronomical subjects of study to which their mathematical powers may be devoted perhaps more successfully than those of our astronomers. For example, the wide sweep of the planet's orbit would enable the Uranians to recognize a displacement of the stars in the course of the long Uranian year. The star Alpha Centauri, which only exhibits to the terrestrial observer an annual parallax of one second, would exhibit to the observer in Uranus a displacement of about the third part of a minute. Other stars would be affected in like proportion, and perhaps the Uranians may thus be enabled to form some conception of that relation which hitherto has proved too baffling a problem to our astronomers—the actual configuration of the nearer parts of the sidereal system. The Neptunians would of course be even more favorably circumstanced.

One difficulty presents itself, however, in thus considering the prospects of the Uranian and Neptunian astronomers. The enormous length of the year of each planet requires that either the astronomers in Uranus and Neptune should be very long-lived, or that they should be very enthusiastic in

the cause of science, to prosecute singly such observations as Henderson, Olbers, or Peters, have
singly prosecuted on our earth. A Uranian who
made one set of observations to determine stellar
parallax when he was, say, twenty-five years old,
would have to wait till he had nearly reached the
threescore years and ten (not perhaps allotted as
the span of Uranian life) before he could make the
corresponding set, by comparing which with the
former, stellar parallax was to be determined. In
Neptune, life must be prolonged over the century
(unless the study of observational astronomy com-
mence during the babyhood of the Neptunians) in
order that a complete set of observations for determining stellar parallax should be carried out. One
cannot but conceive that a certain sluggishness must
mark the progress of astronomy in these far-off
worlds under such circumstances. In fact, the mere
consideration that, after a constellation has passed
away from the nocturnal skies of Uranus or Neptune, thirty or forty years in one case, and seventy
or eighty in the other, must pass before the constellation again becomes favorably visible, suggests
characteristics of astronomical observation altogether
different from those we are familiar with.

Admiral Smyth suggests that these distant planets
must be convenient outposts for watching the approach or recession of comets; but, with all diffidence, I would venture to point out that the inhabitants of the earth are, on the whole, more favorably
situated in this respect. Every large comet which

approaches tolerably near to the sun during perihelion passage is as likely to be seen as to be missed
by the inhabitants of earth; but scarcely one out of
a thousand such comets would be seen from Uranus
or Neptune, since, to be visible, a comet must approach the sun or recede from him along a course
passing tolerably near to the particular position of
either planet at the time; and the chances in the
case of any individual comet would be enormously
against such a contingency.

With eyesight such as ours, the Uranians could
distinctly see Neptune when in opposition, but the
Neptunians would be wholly unable to see Uranus,
or indeed any known planet of the solar system.

Perhaps, though we have very little evidence on
the point, it will be thought more reasonable to suppose that Uranus and Neptune are suns to their
respective systems of satellites, than to imagine that
these two drearily-circumstanced planets are themselves inhabited. Their satellites cannot possibly
compensate, to any noteworthy extent, for the small
amount of solar light or heat which reaches their
primaries. On the other hand, it is not difficult to
conceive that the planets may afford an important
supply of heat (at any rate) to their dependent orbs.
Certainly, so far as the evidence we have extends,
Uranus and Neptune resemble Saturn and Jupiter
too closely not to warrant the application of any
arguments deduced from the appearance of the two
giant planets to the case of their inferior but still
gigantic brethren.

Viewing the matter thus, we seem led to the conclusion that the planets which lie outside the zone
of asteroids are distinguished from those within that
belt, not merely, as had so long been recognized,
in the attributes of size, density, rapidity of rotation,
and complexity of the systems circling around them,
but in this more important and more interesting circumstance, that they and their dependent orbs are
real miniatures of the solar system. Four suns they
would seem to be, not indeed suns resplendent like
the primary sun around which they travel, but still
giving out perhaps no insignificant supply of light;
not heated to incandescence as he is, but still supplying an amount of heat proportionately far greater
than the quantity of light they give forth: in fine,
not, as he is to the inner planets, the sole source
whence all supplies of force are derived, but adding
their influence to his in a variety of complicated but
doubtless well-ordered combinations, in such sort
that the small worlds which circle around them are
provided with all that is needful to the well-being of
their inhabitants.

CHAPTER VIII

THE MOON AND OTHER SATELLITES

ALTHOUGH I do not think that the moon can be regarded as probably at present the abode of life, there are many reasons for studying in a work on other worlds the various relations she presents to us. In the first place, she subserves various useful purposes in the economy of our own earth; then there are circumstances in her appearance which suggest that at one time there may have been life upon her surface; and, lastly, she affords us the only information we have concerning the probable relations presented by the noble systems of moons which circle around Jupiter and the other planets outside the orbit of the asteroids.

Now, with regard to the present habitability of the moon, it may be remarked that we are not justified in asserting positively that no life exists upon her surface. Life has been found under conditions so strange—we have been so often mistaken in assuming that *here* certainly, or *there*, no living creatures can possibly exist—that it would be rash indeed to dogmatize respecting the state of the moon in this respect.

Still, in the case of the moon we have relations wholly different in character from those we have hitherto had to consider. We no longer have to deal with a question of the various degrees of heat and cold, of atmospheric rarity or density, and the like, but with relations which do not in the slightest degree resemble those we are familiar with on earth.

In the first place, the moon has no appreciable atmosphere. We have long known this quite certainly, because we see that when stars are occulted by the moon they disappear instantaneously, whereas we know this would not be the case had the moon an atmosphere of appreciable extent. But if any doubt could have remained, the evidence of the spectroscope in Mr. Huggins's hands would have sufficed to remove it. He has never been able to detect a sign of the existence of any lunar atmosphere, though Mars and Jupiter, so much further from us, have afforded distinct evidence respecting the atmospheres which surround their surface.

Then, secondly, there are no seas or oceans on the moon. Were there any large tracts of water, the tremendous heat to which the moon is subjected during the course of the long lunar day (lasting a fortnight of our time) would certainly cause enormous quantities of water to evaporate; and not only would the effects of this process be distinctly recognizable by our telescopists, but the spectroscope would exhibit in an unmistakable manner the presence of the aqueous vapor thus formed.

Thirdly, there are no lunar seasons. The inclination of the moon's axis to the orbit in which she travels around the sun is nearly 89°, and with this inclination there can be no appreciable seasonal changes.

Fourthly, the enormous length of the lunar day is altogether opposed to our conceptions of what is suitable for animal or vegetable life. The lunar day lasts about a fortnight, and the lunar night is, of course, equally long. Were this all, the inconvenience of the arrangement would be unbearable by beings like ourselves. But far more serious consequences must result from the combination of the arrangement with the want of an atmosphere; for whereas during the lunar day the surface of the moon is exposed to an inconceivably intense direct heat, undoubtedly sufficient to heat that surface far above the boiling-point, during the lunar night the heat is radiated rapidly away into space (no atmosphere checking the process), and an intensity of cold must prevail of which we can form but imperfect conceptions.[1]

---

[1] The moon's physical habitudes are in fact so very different from those of the earth that one cannot read without astonishment the well-known passage in which Sir W. Herschel pleads for the moon's habitability. "Its situation, with respect to the sun," he says, "is much like that of the earth, and by a rotation on its axis it enjoys an agreeable variety of seasons (!) and of day and night. To the moon, our globe will appear to be a very capital satellite, undergoing the same regular changes of illumination as the moon does to the earth. The sun, the planets, and the starry constellations of the heavens, will rise and set there as they do here, and heavy bodies will fall on the moon as they do on the earth. *There seems only to be wanting, in order to complete the analogy, that it should be inhabited like the earth.*" The evidence is, however, all the other way.

The mere fact that our earth is always invisible to three-sevenths of the moon's surface is one which points very strongly to the conclusion that the present condition of the moon is not the one best calculated to meet the wants of living creatures on her surface. In long-past ages, when her rotation had not yet been forced into accordance with her revolution[1] (as at present), the earth must have subserved a variety of most important purposes. If water then existed on the surface of the moon, the earth must have raised tidal waves in her oceans. She must further have reflected enormous supplies of light and heat toward her dependent orb, even if at that time she were not a secondary sun for the lunarians. She must have travelled across the lunar skies as the moon travels over ours, presenting a variety of interesting and beautiful phases affording useful time-measures, and so enabling the travellers on the moon in those long-past ages to guide their course in safety over her oceans or her deserts. But now she is in-

---

[1] The researches of Adams into the peculiarity of the moon's motion, called her acceleration, suffice to show that, under the influence of the moon's attraction on our oceans, the earth's rotation is gradually diminishing; so that, though many millions of ages must elapse first, she will one day so rotate as to keep always the same face turned toward her satellite. We cannot doubt that it has been by a process of this sort that the moon's rotation has been brought to its present rate. In fact, independently of the evidence afforded by the earth's gradual loss of rotation, we cannot account for the moon's peculiarity of rotation without regarding it as due to the earth's controlling influence. A perfectly homogeneous sphere, started on a direct line at the moon's distance, and with the same velocity, would travel without rotation on an orbit like the moon's, and would thus, in completing a revolution, exhibit every part of its surface to us.

visible from a large portion of the moon's surface, and almost a fixture in the skies of those parts, even, of the moon whence she can be seen. Were there lunar oceans, she could raise no tides in them. Were there a lunar atmosphere, she could shed no heat, to be garnered up, so to speak, by that atmosphere, and to compensate, in some sort, for the long absence of the sun.

But have we evidence that at some far-distant epoch the moon was inhabited? Taking for our guidance the analogies which are available to us, can we really conclude that once, in all probability, those barren wastes were clothed with vegetation, those dreary solitudes the abode of life?

When we contemplate with attention the lunar surface, considering the indications it presents of past activities, we are led to inquire how the forces which have been so busily at work were expended. If Nature, studied thoughtfully, teaches us the lesson that there is no form of force which is not the representative of some other preacting form of force, she also teaches us that no form of force ever works without generating other forces as its own energies are expended. The meteor which sweeps with planetary velocity through space may be brought to rest upon the sun, but the energy stored up in its motions is not wasted; the sun may expend the stores of force he derives from meteoric impact, but not idly;[1] all

---

[1] The question may be asked, What becomes of the immense supplies of light and heat continually poured by the sun and other stars into space? We cannot tell; yet we know certainly that they cannot

round us we see the fruits of solar energies, we feel
them within ourselves, we exert them upon others.
And, therefore, when we see on the moon signs that
her surface was at one time upheaved by tremendous
volcanic forces, we are led to the conclusion that between the era when she was thus disturbed, and the
present time, when she seems absolutely quiescent,
there must have been a period when her energies were
employed in sustaining various forms of life. There
has, in this instance, been a process resembling exhaustion, though we know the forms of force which
have passed away from the moon have not really
ceased to exist; but before the lunar forces were dissipated into space, so to speak, they must have subserved that great purpose which seems the end of all
Nature's workings—the support of life.

Associated, however, with this subject, there are
questions of a perplexing character, which invite our

---

be wasted. The heat of Arcturus, measured by Mr. Stone, gives an
account of one large portion of the stellar heat-supplies, because we
know that, small as the amount we receive may be, we must multiply
that amount millions on millions of times to get the total received by all
the orbs in space from this particular sun. But we know that a large
portion of our sun's light and heat must either fail to fall on any other
orbs, or must be gradually exhausted in its progress through space (for,
if lines from the sun in every direction encountered orbs, the sky ought
to be lighted up at all times with star-splendor—which is no other than
sun-splendor). In either case we cannot tell what becomes of the portion seemingly wasted, though in the latter case we may affirm confidently that there is simply a change in the nature of the force. In
both cases we know that the total of force in the universe remains undiminished. There is, indeed, a seeming contradiction here; but it is
not different in character from the seeming contradictions suggested by
the consideration of infinite space and infinite time, which yet we are
compelled to recognize as absolutely as finite space or finite time.

careful consideration. If life ever existed on the moon, that orb must have possessed an atmosphere and seas. Independently, also, of our views on the subject of life upon the moon, we are led, by the revelations of the spectroscope respecting the solar system, to believe that all the bodies within that system are in a general sense similarly constituted; and, if this be so, there must once have been oceans and air upon the moon. What has become of the moon's atmospheric envelope, and of the lunar oceans?

In four several ways this question has been answered. Some have thought that the oceans and air have been withdrawn into cavities within the moon's substance. Others have imagined that the air and oceans may have passed away to the further hemisphere of the moon. According to a third theory, a comet has carried off the lunar oceans and atmosphere. And, lastly, a fourth theory has been maintained, according to which the lunar air, and *a fortiori* the lunar seas, have beeen changed by intensity of cold into the solid form.

Of these theories, the first and last only seem worthy of consideration. We see so much of the moon's further hemisphere during her librations that we must perforce reject the second, even if we had any trustworthy analogy for believing so strange an arrangement to be possible.[1] The third theory is op-

---

[1] Professor Newcombe, of America, has shown excellent reasons for doubting whether even that displacement of the moon's gravity, on which the theory has been based, can be admitted as an established fact. Independently of this, however, the theory will not bear examination. Any one who will draw a cross-section of the moon (in a

posed by all that modern astronomy teaches respecting the constitution of comets.

The theory that an atmosphere formerly surrounding the moon has passed with the lunar oceans into the interior of our satellite has been supported by physicists of considerable eminence. The relatively low specific gravity of the moon (little more than half the earth's) suggests the possibility that cavities large enough to contain even all the waters of our own oceans may exist within the moon. Nor does the fact that we can see no unmistakable signs of chasms extending deep into the moon's substance suffice to render the theory untenable, or even improbable. It is difficult to understand how the inrush of the waters took place. Certainly it cannot have happened while the moon's volcanic forces were in vigorous action; yet a period must undoubtedly have arrived when by little and little the waters could retire within the moon's substance without being vaporized. From what we know of volcanic action on the earth, the lunar volcanoes must have drawn fresh supplies of energy from the gradual influx of water; and one can thus understand why the aspect of the moon indicates that, up to the last moment, so to speak, of her existence as a world, the forces upheaving her crust were busily at work. We can thus see how it has come to pass that the moon's surface shows so few signs of the action of rain or running water.

plane passing through the earth), and endeavor to assign such a position to an atmosphere of moderate extent that, even during the moon's extreme librations, no signs of the atmosphere could be perceptible from the earth, will at once see that the theory is untenable.

The theory that the lunar oceans have become frozen, and that afterward even the gases forming the lunar atmosphere have become solidified, was maintained by Buffon and Bailly in the last century, and has been supported by several astronomers in our own day. In some respects, the aspect of the moon (especially the absence of well-marked colors from her surface) seems to favor the theory. Nor need the excessive heat to which the moon's surface is exposed for weeks at a time be considered a sufficient reason for rejecting it, because we have no means of judging how that heat would act where there is no atmosphere to prevent its immediate and entire reflection into space. We know that, despite the intense heat which is poured upon the summits of the Himalayas, the snow there—though a portion may melt during the day—remains year after year and age after age undiminished; and on the summit of the Himalayas the atmosphere is dense and heavy compared with that which exists even in the lowest abysms of the lunar ravines. If absolute reliance be placed on the results which have been deduced from the application of the great Parsonstown mirror to the measurement of the lunar heat, it would seem as though we must abandon the belief in the existence of frozen oxygen or nitrogen on the moon's surface, since, according to those results, a large proportion of the moon's heat is radiant—in other words, the moon's surface has been actually raised to a high degree of heat by the solar rays. At present, however, physicists are not prepared to look

with perfect confidence on the method by which, in
the researches made at Parsonstown, an attempt has
been made to distinguish between the heat which the
moon reflects and that which she radiates into space.

On the whole, however, the former theory seems
to have the strongest evidence in its favor, or rather
the least decisive evidence against it.

In considering the systems of bodies which circle
around the outer planets, we are struck at once by
several marked circumstances of contrast between their
condition and that of our own moon.

In the first place, we have no satisfactory evidence
that the satellites of Jupiter and Saturn turn always
the same face toward their primary. It is true that
Sir William Herschel was led by certain observations
of the satellites of Jupiter to conclude that this relation holds in their case. But we have far stronger
evidence against such a view, in the fact that modern
observers, armed with telescopes of the most exquisite
defining powers, have not only been unable to confirm the relatively rough observations made by Herschel, but have noticed peculiarities of appearance
only explicable by the theory that the rotation of
the satellites is quite independent of their motion of
revolution around Jupiter. Dawes, for instance, has
observed that the markings seen on the third satellite,
when transiting Jupiter's disk, are variable. Bond
has seen this satellite as a well-defined black spot on
certain occasions, while on others it has appeared
quite bright on the disk of the planet. He once saw
this satellite bright as it entered on the disk of Jupi-

ter, and about half an hour later as a dark spot; while
Mr. Prince, with a powerful reflector, has seen the
satellite dark first and afterward bright. It need
hardly be said that, if the satellite turned always the
same face toward its primary, no such varieties of appearance would be presented during transit. The following passage from Webb's "Celestial Objects" points
strongly also to the conclusion that the rotation of the
Jovial satellites must be independent of their revolution. After mentioning that the variable light of the
satellites may be caused by the existence of spots
upon their surface, he proceeds: "A stranger source
of anomaly has been perceived—the disks themselves
do not always appear of the same size or form. Maraldi noticed the former fact in 1707, Herschel ninety
years afterward inferring also the latter, and both
have since been confirmed. Beer and Mädler, Las-
sell and Secchi, have sometimes seen the disk of the
second satellite larger than that of the first; and Las-
sell, and Secchi and his assistant, have distinctly seen
that of the third satellite irregular and elliptical;
while, according to the Roman observers, the ellipse
does not always lie the same way."

It will easily be seen that these peculiarities indicate the existence of dark markings on these bodies,
and that, as the satellites rotate, the varying position of these markings causes the satellites seemingly to change in figure, since the brighter part of
the satellite would be that which would determine
its apparent figure. And further, since the change
of figure shows no correspondence with the position

of the satellites in their revolution, we infer that
their revolution is independent of their rotation.

It is worthy of notice, however, that even if the
inner satellites turned always the same face toward
their primary, the peculiarity would not (as in the
case of our moon) result in an inordinate lengthening
of their diurnal period, since Jupiter's two inner
satellites complete a revolution in one day eighteen
and a half hours, and three days thirteen hours respectively; while the revolutions of Saturn's five
inner satellites are severally accomplished in twenty-
two and a half hours, one day nine hours, one day
twenty-one hours, two days eighteen hours, and four
days twelve and a half hours.

So far as we can judge from Laplace's estimates,
the specific gravity of Jupiter's moons must be very
small indeed, ranging from one-ninth to four-fifths
of the specific gravity of water. But very little reliance can be placed on these results, because the only
evidence we have respecting the mass of the satellites
is that founded on the perturbations to which their
motions are subjected, and it is very difficult indeed
to estimate these perturbations. When to this we
add the circumstance that little reliance can be placed
on measurements of the minute disks presented by
the satellites, it will be seen that our estimate of the
specific gravities of these bodies cannot by any
means be regarded as trustworthy.

As seen from his satellites, Jupiter must present
a magnificent scene. To the inhabitants, if such
there be, of the innermost satellite, he exhibits a disk

nearly twenty degrees in diameter. Thus, whereas there might be about seven hundred moons such as ours placed all round our horizon, the disk of Jupiter, as seen from the inner satellite, could occupy a full eighteenth part of the horizon's circumference. The disk of Jupiter, as so seen, would cover a space on the heavens exceeding more than fourteen hundred times that which our moon covers. To the second satellite, Jupiter presents a disk about 12½ degrees in diameter, or about six hundred times as large as our moon's. To the third satellite he shows a disk about 7¾ degrees in diameter, or more than two hundred times the size of the moon's. And, lastly, the inhabitants even of the furthermost satellites see him with a diameter of about 4½ degrees—that is, with a disk more than sixty-five times as large as that of our moon. So that, if the views I have put forward respecting Jupiter be correct, the enormous space he covers on the skies of his respective satellites must suffice to compensate in part for the relatively small amount of heat which he can be supposed capable of emitting.

If the satellites rotate with a motion independent of their revolution, Jupiter passes across their skies like a vast moon, exhibiting phases such as those presented by ours, but on a far vaster scale. But, besides his phases, he must exhibit to the inhabitants of his satellites the most marvellous picture that can be conceived. His belts' changes of figure and color, only rendered visible to our astronomers by powerful telescopic aid, must be distinctly visible to creatures

on his satellites, and cannot but afford reasoning beings on those orbs a most astounding theme for study
and admiration.

To the inhabitants of the satellites which circle
around Saturn, the ringed planet must present an
even more interesting spectacle. His disk, as seen
from the nearest of his satellites, has a diameter of 17
degrees, and an apparent surface exceeding more than
nine hundred times that of the moon. From the furthest satellite his disk is less than a degree in diameter, and therefore not quite four times as large as our
moon's. Between these limits the apparent size of
Saturn varies as we pass from satellite to satellite;
but from the sixth satellite his apparent surface is
twenty-five times, while from the seventh it is sixteen times, as large as the moon's; so that the outer
satellite is quite exceptionally circumstanced in this
respect.

It is not so much from the apparent size of his
disk, however (though in the case of all the inner
satellites that must be a most remarkable relation),
as from the peculiar character of his ring-system,
that Saturn must derive his chief interest. It is
true that the inner satellites travel nearly in the
plane of the rings, so as always to see them nearly
edgewise. But, even so viewed, the rings must present a most striking appearance. From the inner
satellite, indeed, the extreme span of the ring-system
must be more than ninety degrees;[1] so that when

---

[1] About 93° according to the best estimates of the dimensions of the
rings and the distance of the satellite.

one extremity is seen on the horizon the system
would appear as an arch thickest in the middle, extending over an arc of about ninety-three degrees,
and having the disk of Saturn at its centre. When
the whole of this arch is illuminated, Saturn is
"full"; at other times he presents all the phases
shown by our moon, and the arch of light is correspondingly shortened. Saturn "full" and in the
zenith, with the ring-system dependent on either side
of his disk, must be a glorious spectacle as seen
from certain regions of his innermost satellite. The
display would diminish in grandeur, though not
perhaps in interest, as seen from satellites further
and further away. But the inhabitants of the outermost satellite of all have the privilege of seeing the
Saturnian ring-system opened out much more fully
than as seen from the other satellites, since the path
of this moon is inclined some fifteen degrees to the
plane of the ring.

Of the satellites of Uranus and Neptune little can
be said, because so little is known either respecting
these orbs themselves or their primaries. I may
remark that, despite the evidence brought forward
to the contrary, I have very little doubt that Uranus
has at least eight satellites. Four of those discovered by Sir W. Herschel have not indeed been yet
identified; but one cannot read the account of his
method of procedure without feeling that no amount
of mere negative evidence can be opposed effectively
to the positive information he has left respecting
these four orbs. Indeed, when we remember that

Uranus is twice as far from us as Saturn, while it has only been in recent times that the eighth Saturnian satellite (the seventh in position) has been discovered, we cannot but consider that in all probability many more Uranian satellites will one day be discovered. Neptune also, no doubt, has a large family of satellites circling around him.

CHAPTER IX

METEORS AND COMETS: THEIR OFFICE IN THE SOLAR SYSTEM

THERE are few more interesting chapters in the history of astronomy than that which deals with the gradual introduction of meteors into an important position in the economy of the solar system. Regarded for a long time as simply atmospheric phenomena (though many ancient philosophers held another opinion), it has only been after a long and persistent series of researches that they have come at length to be regarded in their true light. But, though the history of those researches is not only full of interest, but highly instructive and encouraging, this is not the place for entering at length into its details. I must present facts and conclusions, rather than the narrative of observations or calculations by which those facts and conclusions have been established. Nay, it would seem at first sight as though even the nature of meteors could have very little to do with the subject of this treatise, since we cannot suppose these small bodies to be inhabited worlds. It will be found, however, that, though this is certainly true, there are reasons for

believing that meteors are associated in a very intimate manner with the general relations of the scheme
of worlds forming the solar system.

Under the head "Meteors" I include all those
objects which reach the earth's atmosphere from
without, whether they actually make their way to
her surface unbroken, like the aërolites; or explode
into small fragments, as bolides and fire-balls have
been observed to do; or are apparently consumed in
traversing the upper regions of the air, as happens
with shooting or falling stars. All these objects, we
now know, represent in reality bodies of greater or
less size, which, before their encounter with the
earth, were travelling around the sun in orbits of
greater or less eccentricity The larger masses,
though they must be very numerous (or our earth
would not once in many ages encounter any of
them), are yet relatively few in number as compared
with fire-balls, and still more so in comparison with
shooting-stars. It has been calculated, indeed, that
these last are so numerous that the earth, in passing
through a region of space equal to her own dimensions, must encounter no less than thirteen thousand
of them; while of yet smaller bodies, whose passage
through our air would only be recognizable by telescopic aid, she is supposed to encounter as many as
forty thousand within a similar space. Without lay-
ing great stress on these calculations, we may yet feel
quite sure that the earth must encounter enormous
numbers of these bodies, from the mere fact that,
though at any fixed station but a minute slice (so to

speak) of the earth's atmosphere is within view, and even but a portion only of that slice visible to a single observer, six or seven falling stars on the average may be seen during each hour of the night.

It will be seen, then, that a problem of the utmost importance was involved in the question whether these bodies came from the interplanetary spaces, or from the region of space over which the earth's own attractive energies prevail. Now that we know the former view to be the true one, we recognize the fact that, though each meteor may be individually insignificant, the meteors of the solar system, looked on as a single family, form a highly-interesting and important portion of the solar system.

But now a yet more significant relation has to be considered. Regarding meteors as planetary bodies, they might yet be relatively unimportant, if we had any reason to believe that they form a sort of zone or belt near the earth's orbit, resembling in a sense the asteroidal zone, only composed of far smaller constituent bodies. We could not *then* argue, from the number of meteors encountered in a given time by the earth, the largeness of the total number of these bodies; for it might well be that this zone had no counterpart, either in the outer part of the planetary system or within the orbit of the earth. What has actually been discovered, however, respecting the paths along which the meteoric bodies have reached the earth, immensely enhances the importance of these objects.

It has been proved, on evidence perfectly incon-

testable, that two well-marked meteoric systems travel
in orbits of enormous eccentricity. The August meteors travel on a path so eccentric that in the neighborhood of the earth's orbit it may be regarded as
almost parabolic in figure. That it is not absolutely
parabolic is shown, of course, by the fact that a period
has been assigned to the revolution of the members of
the zone. No observations have been indeed made
by which astronomers could determine the orbit of
these meteors, since for this purpose an exact determination of the velocity with which they enter the
earth's atmosphere would be requisite, while the observations actually made to determine their velocity
are confessedly inexact. But an association, altogether too close to be regarded as accidental, has
been discovered between their orbit and that of a
bright comet which appeared in 1862, and this, combined with what has since been established respecting
the relations between comets and meteors, enables astronomers to adopt quite confidently the orbit of the
comet as that of the meteoric system. Now, a period
of one hundred and forty-five years implies, according
to Kepler's law, an orbit having a mean distance nearly
equal to that of Neptune. And since the orbit is so
eccentric as to bring these bodies close by the earth
when they are near perihelion, it follows that their
aphelion distance must exceed their mean distance in
the same degree. Hence the aphelion point of the
August meteors must lie nearly twice as far away
from us as the orbit of Neptune.

The November meteors have been shown in like

manner to travel in a period of thirty-three and a quarter years around the sun, the aphelion of their orbit lying far beyond the path of Uranus.

So far, then, as we can judge from the only two meteoric systems whose orbits can be said to have been satisfactorily determined (though there are many other systems which have been associated with known comets), we are led to the conclusion that the meteoric orbits are for the most part eccentric. We know, further, that they are inclined in all directions to the plane in which the earth travels, because we see that their constituent bodies fall upon the earth in directions which show no tendency to near coincidence with the ecliptic.

Now, these two circumstances are full of meaning. If the meteors travelled in nearly circular orbits, at a mean distance nearly equal to the earth's mean distance from the sun, then the earth would be certain to encounter meteors in the course of her orbital motion round the sun. Again, if the meteors travelled in eccentric orbits, whose perihelia lay within the earth's orbit, and if these orbits all lay in or near the plane of the earth's path, the earth could not fail to encounter meteors as she travelled round the sun. But under the actual circumstances—the mean distances of the meteoric orbits being in no way associated with the earth's mean distance, and the inclination of these orbits to the ecliptic not being in any way limited—the two questions are at once suggested: 1. What is the *a priori* chance that the earth would encounter the members of any meteoric system taken at random? and, 2. If this chance be small, what is the conclusion to be drawn from the fact that the earth encounters meteors belonging to many systems?—the number already recognized being nearly sixty. Now, assigning elements at random to a meteor-system, we see that, unless the resulting orbit actually coincides with the plane of the ecliptic (a relation which would not happen in a million trials), the orbit will intersect that plane in two points, lying on a straight line through the sun. And, for the earth to encounter members of the meteoric system, it is requisite that one or other of these two points shall lie close to the earth's orbit. But these points may have any position whatever in the plane of the ecliptic, and the chance that one of them has the requisite position may be regarded as indefinitely small. It follows then that the *a priori* chance of the earth's encountering the members of a meteoric system is indefinitely small; and hence we conclude that the number of meteoric systems she passes wholly clear of is indefinitely great, in comparison with the number whose members she encounters. But she actually encounters meteors belonging to no less than fifty-six systems: hence the total number of meteoric systems belonging to the planetary scheme must be an indefinitely large multiple of the number fifty-six, or, in other words, it must be enormously beyond our powers of conception.

But this being so, it behooves us to inquire, first of all, what extent we must assign to individual meteoric systems, and how densely we may suppose meteoric masses to be strewn along each system; and,

secondly, what may be the nature, quality, and substance of these meteoric masses. For we clearly
begin to see that we are in the presence of relations
which may—or, I should rather say, which must—
affect most importantly the economy of the solar
system.

Now, we have seen something already of the longitudinal extent of meteoric systems, since that extent
corresponds to the circumference of meteoric orbits,
and we have seen that these orbits have enormous
dimensions. We may, indeed, suppose that in some
cases the whole extent of an orbit is not occupied by
meteoric masses at any one instant; but even when,
as in the case of the November meteors, the annual
displays wax and wane in splendor, there is no absolute cessation in the occurrence of star-falls on the
date corresponding to such a system. And taking full
account even of the marked diminution which actually
occurs, we are yet compelled to assign an enormous
longitudinal extent to that portion of the system
which has been poetically termed "the gem of the
meteor-ring." For example, in the November meteor-
system, this portion of the ring cannot be less than
1,000,000,000 of miles in length. As to the width of
a meteor-system—that is, its extent in a direction
measured in the plane of its orbit—we have no satisfactory information, because a meteor-system may extend enormously on either side of the point through
which the earth's orbit intersects it, and yet no trace
of that extension be recognized by observers on the
earth. Still we may conclude that this dimension lies

in extent somewhere between the longitudinal extension of the system and the depth of the meteor-zone—
that is, the length of a line taken through its square
to the plane in which it lies. Now, of this last dimension we can form a tolerably accurate estimate in
many instances. We know that so long as meteors
belonging to any system are flashing into view, our
earth is still plunging through the system; and if we
know the position of the system we can determine its
depth in this way, just as we could determine the
breadth of a range of hills if we noticed how long a
train, travelling with known velocity, took in passing
through a tunnel which traversed the range of hills
in a known direction. Judged in this way, the depth
of the November meteor-zone would seem to be one
hundred thousand miles in the part traversed by the
earth in 1866, about sixty thousand miles in the part
traversed in 1867, and considerably greater (though
the zone was more sparsely strewn with meteors)
where the earth crossed the system in 1868 and 1869.

Now, as regards the density with which meteors
are strewn in any known system, I must remark on
a mistake which has been very commonly made. It
has been thought necessary to consider the velocity
with which the meteors themselves travel as well as
the earth's velocity, in order to determine, from the
average interval of time separating the appearance of
successive meteors, the average distance separating
neighboring meteors from each other. This, however, is an erroneous mode of dealing with the problem. We need only consider the earth's velocity,

since the meteoric motions cannot possibly tend to increase the total number of encounters.[1] Let us apply this consideration to enable us to form a rough estimate of the number of bodies in the richer part of the November meteor-system. We may fairly assume that, taking the average of the four displays of the years 1866–69, the earth encountered more than one meteor per minute as she swept successively through the system; or, conveniently for our purpose, that an average distance of 1,000 miles separates meteor from meteor throughout the "gem of the ring." Now, the length of the great cluster is at least 1,000,000,000 miles, its thickness may be fairly assumed as averaging 100,000 miles, and its width can hardly be less than ten times its thickness, since the forces acting on the system tend much more largely to affect its width than its thickness. Thus, with the assumed average of distance (1,000 miles), we find that the cluster cannot contain less than (1,000,000 × 100 × 1,000) or one hundred thousand million members.

Mr. Alexander Herschel, from observations of the amount of light given out by these bodies, and a calculation founded on the velocity with which they

[1] Obviously the total number of meteors encountered during the earth's passage through a meteor-stream will be the number contained in a cylindrical space having a cross-section equal to the earth's, and traversing the meteor-stream from side to side. The motion of the meteors will affect the particular set of meteors actually found within this space as the earth traverses it, but will not affect their number, assuming a general uniformity of meteoric distribution.

penetrate our atmosphere, has come to the conclusion that they must, for the most part, be very small, rarely, perhaps, exceeding a few ounces in weight. We shall certainly not exaggerate their weight if we assign one-hundredth part of an ounce to each. We thus obtain for the weight of the whole cluster one thousand millions of ounces, or about twenty-eight thousand tons. The actual weight of the November meteor-system cannot, however, but enormously exceed this amount; and therefore we recognize how erroneous that opinion is which an eminent astronomer recently expressed, who asserted that the united weight of all the bodies other than planets in the solar system must be estimated rather by pounds than by tons. We have certainly no reason for thinking that the November system, though one of the most important encountered by the earth, is exceptionally important in the solar system. On the contrary, we have every reason the laws of probability can afford us, for believing that there must be millions of systems equally or more extensive. And, further, the fall of enormous masses, many tons sometimes in weight, upon the earth, would point to the conclusion that the members of the November system are exceptionally insignificant as regards their individual dimensions. So that we seem forced to the conclusion that the aggregate weight of the various meteoric systems circulating around the sun must be estimated by billions of tons rather than by any of our ordinary units.

I have already referred to the relation which has

been detected between comets and meteor-systems. *Bizarre* as the relation appears, it has been established on evidence which cannot reasonably be disputed. It carries with it results of extreme interest and importance.

I do not propose here to enter into any consideration of those enormously difficult questions which are suggested by the study of cometic phenomena. That they will before very long receive their solution, I confidently believe; but in the present state of our knowledge it would indeed be hazardous to speculate as to what that solution may be. I may remark in passing, that, while I recognize in Dr. Tyndall's recently-promulgated theory on the subject the indication of a highly-suggestive and promising line of research, I cannot but feel that cometic phenomena are far too complicated to be directly accounted for in the way pointed out by that distinguished physicist. Some of the more obvious, and, I may add, the more generally known phenomena, do indeed appear to receive a solution when examined under the light of Dr. Tyndall's researches, but numbers of others remain not only unaccounted for, but standing apparently altogether opposed to his theory.[1]

But for my present purpose the facts to be principally noticed are in a sense independent of any theory which may be formed respecting the nature of

---

[1] The theory recently put forward by Professor Tait is altogether inconsistent with the history of many comets. Indeed, I have been unable to find a single comet whose recorded changes of appearance countenance Professor Tait's views.

comets. We know that the dimensions of these objects are in many cases enormous. We know, further,
that there must be many thousands of comets remaining undiscovered for each that our astronomers have
detected. And, lastly, we are led to recognize the observed association between certain meteor-systems and
certain comets as indicative of a general law by which,
in some way as yet unexplained, comets and meteors
are associated together. Thus, independently of the
considerations already adduced, we are led to the conclusion that meteor-systems must be very numerous;
while from the fact that a meteor-system so important
as the November stream is associated with a comet so
insignificant as Tempel's, we conclude that those magnificent comets which have blazed in our skies—a
source at once of wonder and perplexity to the astronomer—must be associated with systems of bodies
incalculably more important than the meteor-system
which has so often filled the heavens with falling
stars.

Now, combining all these results, we seem fairly
led to the conclusion that purposes of the utmost importance in the economy of the solar system must be
subserved by these uncounted thousands of meteoric
streams. If, indeed, we could suppose that the planets steered clear of them, and that the bodies composing them simply circulated unceasingly in their orbits,
we might form another opinion. But we know that
meteors are continually falling upon the atmosphere of
our own earth, either there to be dissipated into finest
dust or to pass onward, with or without explosion, to

the actual surface of the earth; and we cannot doubt that in a similar way countless thousands of meteors are falling, not only upon all the primary members of the solar system, but upon asteroids and satellites— nay, are even streaming in among the minute bodies composing the rings of Saturn. These encounters cannot be wholly without result, and it is quite conceivable that most injurious consequences might ensue to the inhabitants of all the worlds in the solar system if the continual supply of meteoric matter were importantly diminished.

Now, if meteoric masses fall continually upon the planets, such masses must fall in numbers inconceivably greater upon the sun; and it is here, unless I mistake, that the great purpose of the meteoric systems becomes apparent.

Let us clearly recognize, however, why and how the sun must be assaulted by a continual inrush of meteoric bodies. We have seen how enormous must be the number of these bodies; we know how swiftly they travel, and on what eccentric orbits; but we must go further before we can prove that they fall upon the sun. For example, the November meteors are enormous in number, and travel with enormous velocity in a very eccentric orbit, but they do not approach the sun within a distance of nearly ninety millions of miles. Nor, indeed, can any known meteoric system pour a steady hail of meteors, so to speak, upon the sun; for he is the ruling centre of every meteoric system, and therefore under ordinary circumstances the meteoric orbits must pass around

him, and not in such a direction as to intersect his
substance.

But it is to be remembered that meteors must be
infinitely more crowded in the neighborhood of the
sun than at a distance from him. An indefinitely
large number of meteoric orbits must absolutely intersect in the immediate neighborhood of the sun;
and collisions must continually be taking place as
countless thousands of meteoric flights rush toward
and past and then away from their perihelia. Where
these perihelia lie close to the sun, the velocity with
which the meteors travel must exceed two hundred
miles per second, and therefore the collision even
of two minute meteors must result in the genera-
tion of an enormous amount of light and heat. But
that is not all. Among the collisions thus continually taking place in the sun's neighborhood there
must be a considerable proportion in which the two
bodies are brought momentarily almost to rest by
the shock. In such cases the combined mass of the
two meteors would fall directly upon the sun, a fresh
supply of light and heat being generated as they
were brought again to rest upon his surface.

Whether in the continual collisions of meteors
among themselves, and in their precipitation upon
the sun's surface, we have a sufficient explanation
of the seemingly exhaustless emission of light and
heat from the sun, I should not care positively to
assert. Professor Thompson, who was one of the
first to adopt this view, has, I believe, abandoned it;
though it is worthy of remark that the strongest evi-

dence in its favor has been obtained since he with-
drew his support from it, or at least admitted that
the downfall of meteors on the sun's surface is not
alone sufficient to account for the solar light and
heat. But I am quite certain that there is no flaw
in the evidence I have adduced from the laws of
probability; and that we are bound to accept, as a
legitimate conclusion from that evidence, the theory
that at least an important proportion of the sun's
heat is supplied from the meteoric streams which
circulate in countless millions around him. I believe that, without adopting any unreasonable assump-
tions, it might readily be shown that the whole even
of that enormous supply of light and heat which the
sun emits on every side is derived from the meteoric
streams belonging to the solar system or drawn in
from surrounding space, as the sun, attended by his
family of planets, sweeps onward amid the stellar
groups.

If this view be correct, then the meteor-systems
constitute, indeed, a most important part of the
sun's domain. They may be said almost to share
with the sun a title to be regarded as the source of
all the forms of force which exist throughout the
solar system. If, in the energies of living creatures
on earth, in the forces derived from the fuel that
propels our engines, or in the power of winds and
storms, we trace the action of the ruling centre of
the solar system, we may trace back the chain
of causation yet one link further, and see in the
sun's emission of light and heat the result of forces

inherent in the meteoric systems which circle around him.

But we must not forget one most important consideration, which makes the sun (as might be anticipated) again the chief source of all the forms of force existing within his system. The motions of the meteoric masses are almost wholly due to the sun's attraction; and therefore, in so far as those motions are to be regarded as a means of renewing the solar heat, we must regard the sun's attractive energy as the source whence his heat and all the other forms of force which he exerts are in reality derived.

Yet one step further. The sun's attractive energies might be increased a thousand-fold, and yet not avail to supply the various forms of force which are required by his dependent worlds, were there no external material on which those energies could act in such sort as to lead to the continual inrush of matter upon the solar surface. Nor would it suffice if such materials, even in enormous quantities, existed *close* to the sun. It is the distance from which that material is dragged toward the sun which gives that orb the power of imparting those tremendous velocities to which the collisions of the meteoric bodies owe their real effectiveness. We thus find in *distance*, in the simple element of *scale*, the true source of the various forms of force which are continually exerted throughout the solar system. The sun surrounded by millions on millions of meteoric masses close at hand would be powerless, but placed as ruler over a space far wider than the sphere circled by Neptune's orbit, amid which space those countless millions of meteors are distributed, he becomes forthwith the centre of a thousand forms of force, gathered by him continually from the systems of meteors circling around him, and distributed by him abundantly and without ceasing to his dependent worlds.[1]

It will not fail to be noticed by the thoughtful reader that, adopting this view of the relation in which meteoric and cometic systems stand with respect to the sun, it seems necessary that we should regard those planets which I have endeavored to raise to the dignity of secondary suns, as subordinate centres of attraction, around which countless thousands of meteoric systems may be supposed to circle. Have we any evidence pointing to such a conclusion?

Now, there can be no doubt that if Jupiter, the nearest of these secondary suns, did so act upon a passing comet as to compel that body to circle in future around *him*, instead of pursuing its course around the sun, we could not in any way become conscious of the event unless the comet were an ex-

---

[1] Just as this work was about to be placed in the printer's hands I received from Professor Kirkwood, of America, one of his valuable contributions to the history of the solar system. In it he points to the evidence we have that the sun, as he speeds onward through space, passes through regions in which cometic and meteoric materials are now richly, now sparsely strewn, and gathers in accordingly new stores of force of greater or less amount. The bearing of the views of this acute and soundly-reasoning astronomer (the Kepler of our day), not only on the theories dealt with in the above chapter, but on those considered in the chapters which follow, will be seen at once.

ceptionally large one. I conceive, however, that such an event, though undoubtedly possible,[1] must be so uncommon that the number of cometic systems thus forced to own Jupiter as their centre of attraction must be relatively few. But in another way the planet does exhibit his power as a comet-ruler, making comets recognize him as a sort of subordinate master, the sun being their primary ruler. When comets coming from outer space pass near enough to Jupiter, he sways them so markedly from the orbit they are pursuing that the scene of encounter becomes the aphelion of their orbit, or nearly so. Thence they pass on their new orbit to their perihelion, returning again presently to the scene of their encounter with Jupiter, and so revolving in an orbit having its aphelion close by the orbit of Jupiter, until haply the giant is again near the scene of

---

[1] It is necessarily possible in the case of any planet, but must in many cases be highly improbable. For example, astronomers sometimes assert that meteoric masses passing near the earth might become satellites of hers, but in reality this is a very unlikely event, because the maximum velocity which a body travelling under the earth's influence can have (that is, the velocity acquired by a body travelling from infinity to a perigee close to the earth) is less than the velocity with which a body circling on any orbit round the sun would move when at the earth's distance from him, unless its orbit were very eccentric and the aphelion close by the earth's orbit. Bodies travelling from outer space toward the sun cannot by any possibility become satellites of the earth, because they would always have a velocity greater than that which her attraction can master. Even in the rare event of their grazing her atmosphere, and so losing a large share of their velocity, they could not become permanent satellites of hers, because, returning to the scene of encounter, they would lose yet a larger share of their velocity, and so must be brought, and that soon, to her surface.

encounter at the moment when the comet comes back to it. In this case a fresh struggle takes place, the overmastering attraction of the planet necessarily prevailing, and the comet being often dismissed on a new orbit, whose perihelion, instead of its aphelion, lies close by the orbit of Jupiter.

Now, we know that such events as these must be of frequent occurrence as Jupiter sweeps swiftly round on his orbit. For we recognize several comets which have evidently been compelled by Jupiter to take up such orbits as I have spoken of—a family of comets, in fact, including Encke's, Faye's, and Brorsen's comets, Winnecke's short-period comet, and several others. We judge further, from the laws of probability, that, for each discovered comet of this family, there must be thousands which have escaped detection. So that around the orbit of Jupiter (if not around Jupiter himself) there cling the aphelia of myriads of cometic orbits, whose perihelia lie at all conceivable distances from the sun less than the distance of Jupiter.

Saturn also has his family of comets; so also have Uranus and Neptune. The comet associated with the November meteors belongs indeed to the Uranian comet family, and the epoch (126 A.D.) has even been pointed out when this comet fell under the dominion (subject always to the sun's superior control) of that distant planet.

And here I may refer to a view which I have long entertained respecting the purposes which meteoric and cometic systems have fulfilled in the past history of the solar system.[1] We know that the materials composing meteors, and we conclude, therefore, that those composing comets, do not differ from those which constitute the earth and sun, and presumably the planets also. Therefore, under the continual rain of meteoric matter, it may be said that the earth, sun, and planets, are *growing*. Now, the idea obviously suggests itself, that the whole growth of the solar system, from its primal condition to its present state, may have been due to processes resembling those which we now see taking place within its bounds. It is of course obvious that, if this be so, the number of meteoric and cometic systems must have been enormously greater originally than it is at present. Countless millions of meteoric systems, travelling in orbits of every degree of eccentricity and inclination, travelling also in all conceivable directions around the centre of gravity of the whole, would go to the making up of each individual planet. A marked tendency to aggregate around one definite plane, and to move in directions which, referred to that plane, corresponded to the present direction of planetary motion, would suffice to account for the present state of things. The effect of multiplied collisions would

[1] Since the present chapter was written, I find that the hypothesis here put forward, has, in a general way, been touched on by more than one astronomer and physicist. I believe, however, that here, for the first time, it has been associated with the chief features of the solar system. It was suggested in note B (Appendix) to my treatise on Saturn. But, as a matter of fact, when that note was written, as also when those passages were published in which the same hypothesis is touched by other authors, the decisive evidences in favor of the theory were wanting.

necessarily be to eliminate orbits of exaggerated eccentricity, and to form systems travelling nearly on the mean plane of the aggregate motions, and with a direct motion. Further, where collisions were most numerous, there would be found not only the most circular resulting orbits, not only the greatest approach to exact coincidence of such orbits with the mean plane of the whole system, but the bodies formed out of the resulting systems would there exhibit rotations coinciding most nearly with the mean plane of the entire system.[1]

It seems to me that, not only has this general view of the mode in which our system has reached its present state a greater support from what is now actually going on than the nebular hypothesis of Laplace, but that it serves to account in a far more satisfactory manner for the principal peculiarities of the solar system. I might indeed go further, and say that, where these peculiarities seem to oppose themselves to Laplace's theory, they give support to that which I have put forward.

For example, what is there in the nebular hypothesis which affords even a general explanation of the strange varieties of size observed in the planetary system? How can that hypothesis be reconciled with the remarkable variations of inclination observed

---

[1] This conclusion depends on a well-known law of probability. It may be thus illustrated: If we have in a bag a hundred white and a hundred black balls, and take out at random a number of balls, then the larger that number, the more nearly (in all probability) will the number of black and white balls included in it approach to a ratio of equality.

among the planets, or with the retrograde and almost perpendicular motion of the satellites of Uranus?
Nor, again, is the hypothesis consistent with the
observed peculiarities of motion of those meteoric
systems which we must now regard as regular members of the solar system.

Now, according to the hypothesis I have put forward above, a general explanation of all these matters is at once suggested.   Let us consider:

In the neighborhood of the great central aggregation which would undoubtedly result from the motions of such meteoric systems as I have considered,
all the motions would be very rapid.   They would,
in fact, resemble the motions now actually observed
in the sun's neighborhood.   Here, therefore, subordinate aggregations would form with difficulty, since
they would have small power of overruling meteoric
systems rushing with so great a velocity past them.
In the sun's immediate neighborhood, then, we should
expect to find relatively small planets; and we do
accordingly find that Mercury, nearest to him, is the
smallest of the planets, Venus larger, and the earth
(yet further away) not only larger than Venus, but
adorned with an attendant satellite.

Now, at a much greater distance from the sun the
meteoric motions would be so much less, that here,
supposing only a suitable mean density of aggregation, it would be possible for subordinate centres of
aggregation of far greater magnitude to form.   These
centres would increase in importance as they swept
round the central aggregation, continually gathering

fresh recruits. Indeed, though, *as now*, they would not be able to prevent the major part of the materials rushing from outer space toward the sun from aggregating round *him*, they would still gather in no inconsiderable portion of those materials. Where the largest portion would be gathered would depend on the way in which (taking a general view of the system) the quantity of material increased toward the neighborhood of the centre. For clearly, while distance from the sun would increase the facility with which materials would be gathered in—since the sun's influence would diminish with distance, it would also affect the quantity of material available—since, from a very early period, the system must have begun to show an appearance resembling that now presented by the zodiacal light, that is, a general increase of density toward the centre.

Assuming that the region of maximum aggregation was that where the influence of the ruling centre first became so far diminished with distance as to render the formation of a great subordinate aggregation possible, we should have the innermost of the outer series of planets also the most bulky; and next, within that giant planet we should find a relatively barren space, cleared of material not only by the sun's still powerful influence, but also by the influence of this first important subordinate aggregation. The initial assumption is, in itself, at least not improbable, and, having once admitted it, we find an explanation of the giant mass of Jupiter, of the comparative poverty of material just within the

orbit of Jupiter, and hence, of the condition of the
asteroidal zone, and of the smallness of the planet
Mars next within that zone—though this planet far
outweighs (according to Leverrier's estimate) the
united mass of all the asteroids. Beyond the orbit
of Jupiter, we should expect (after passing an enormously wide space, bare of worlds) to find still a
great abundance of material, and an even greater
facility in the aggregation of that material. Thus
the existence of the planet Saturn, next in importance to Jupiter, and surpassing him in the complexity of his attendant system, is accounted for; yet
further away we look for and find still an abundance of material, and that material somewhat more
uniformly strewn, while the sun's small influence is
indicated by the existence of satellites, of which
doubtless many more will one day be discovered by
astronomers.

And as to the rotations of the various members
of the solar system we find some account, necessarily
not exact, given by this theory. I have mentioned
above the results to be looked for; those observed
are closely accordant with that view. Thus the sun,
the largest member of the system, and specially pre-
eminent within its inner division, rotates on an axis
inclined but about seven degrees to the mean plane
of the system. Mars, the least member of this system, has an inclination of no less than twenty-eight
degrees; the larger earth an inclination of but
twenty-three degrees. The inclinations of Venus and
Mercury are undetermined; they may be expected

to be large, not merely on account of the smallness
of these bodies, but on account of their proximity to
the sun. Of the outer division of the system, Jupiter, the largest, has an inclination of little more
than three degrees; Saturn has a very considerable
inclination (more than twenty-six degrees); Uranus
has an inclination which may be described as actually greater than ninety degrees, since he rotates
backward with his equator inclined seventy-six degrees to the ecliptic. And lastly, if the observations
hitherto made on Neptune's satellites are to be
trusted, this planet, probably, rotates in a retrograde manner, his equator being inclined some
twenty-six degrees to the horizon; so that, to render
the comparison between his rotation and that of the
other members of the solar system complete, he may
be said to rotate in a direct manner with his equator
inclined some one hundred and fifty-four degrees to
the ecliptic.

The great inclination and eccentricity of many of
the asteroidal orbits are also accounted for more
satisfactorily by this theory than by the nebular
hypothesis. In fact, there is an absolute incorrect-
ness in the assertion that the smallness of the asteroids can (on the ordinary view of their origin) explain the relatively irregular nature of their motions.
Their minuteness doubtless brings them more under
the disturbing influence of Jupiter than a single
massive planet at the same distance from the sun
would be. But the attractions of Jupiter can have
no influence in causing the asteroids to depart so

widely as they do from the ecliptic, since his path lies quite close to the ecliptic, and even nearer to the mean plane of the solar system. But bodies formed as the asteroids are supposed to be, according to the hypothesis I have suggested, would necessarily exhibit a much greater variety of motion than would be recognized in the case of the larger planets.

Another point in which, as I conceive, my hypothesis is more satisfactory than the nebular one, consists in the fact that it suggests an explanation of the peculiarities observed in the planetary periods. Professor Kirkwood's researches into the various relations of commensurability presented among the periods of planets and satellites, and the known effects of commensurability in encouraging the accumulation of planetary perturbations, will at once suggest to the mathematical reader the way in which a system, forming in such a manner as I have imagined, might be expected to exhibit the presence of law as regards distances and periods. I know of nothing in the nebular hypothesis which encourages the belief that a system framed as Laplace conceived the solar system to be, would exhibit any such laws as are found within the planetary scheme.

The hypothesis I have put forward also gets rid of that which has always seemed to me the great difficulty of the nebular hypothesis. According to the views of Laplace, Neptune must have been formed millions of ages before Uranus, Uranus as long before Saturn, Saturn as long before Jupiter, and so on. Now, we know that the appearance of those primary members of the solar system which we are best able to study does not indicate any such enormous disproportion in the ages of the planets, even if it does not indicate that the planets were formed nearly at the same era. According to my hypothesis, the various processes of aggregation would go on simultaneously (just as the influences which Jupiter ·has on comets are *now* exerted simultaneously with those more powerful influences possessed by the sun); and though the various orbs formed by those processes would not necessarily be completed simultaneously, there would be no such enormous disproportion in their age as is necessary according to the theory of Laplace.

Yet another strong point in favor of this hypothesis resides in the circumstance that we now have every reason to believe that all the planets are constituted of the same elements. When it was thought that Jupiter might be a watery globe, for instance, there was some evidence in favor of Laplace's theory. But we now know that Jupiter is not constituted differently, in all probability, from the earth and sun, as according to Laplace's theory he must have been. Since, then, we know that meteors contain the same elements which exist in the constitution of sun and planets, we have here a very strong argument in favor of the view that they have played the important part I have assigned to them in the formation of the solar system.

But, after all, the strongest evidence in favor of the hypothesis I have suggested, consists in the fact

that the processes by means of which I conceive the
solar system to have been formed are undoubtedly
going on before our eyes. There may be little, indeed, in the downfall of meteoric showers to suggest
the idea of world-formation or sun-formation; little
in the present aspect of the zodiacal light or of the
solar corona to present to the mind's eye a picture
of that vaster agglomeration of meteoric and 'cometic
systems, all speeding with inconceivable velocities
on their interlacing orbits, which I imagine to have
been the embryon of the solar scheme. But sun and
planets *are* growing, however slowly, as the meteoric
hail falls continuously upon them; the zodiacal light
and the solar corona *are* doubtless due to the existence of meteoric systems, resembling (however relatively insignificant) those which I have pictured as
the materials of the planetary scheme. In the Saturnian rings, also, which have been proved by the
researches of Maxwell and others to consist of multitudes of discrete bodies, we have evidence of the
same sort in the case of a subordinate centre of aggregation. So that we have a form of evidence which
was wanting in the case of the nebular hypothesis,
in favor of this other hypothesis, by which, as in
Laplace's, the present state of the solar system is
regarded as the result of a process of development,
and not of special creative fiats of the Almighty.

In this last respect, the hypothesis I have put forward will doubtless seem objectionable to those who
imagine that, in indicating processes according to
which the solar system may have reached its present

condition, astronomers are attacking the attributes of God. This will be the more unfortunate, because those who entertain this strange view may be regarded as probably so far beyond the reach of argument as to be unlikely ever to abandon their objection. Otherwise, it might avail to point out that, as, in all that surrounds us, we find God acting through second causes, we can have no reason for assigning limits to the range of space or time within which He so acts; that is, we can have no reason for believing that we can point to a time when He acted *directly* upon the universe: and further, that it gives an altogether higher idea of that wisdom which must, in any case, be far above our conceptions, to regard the laws of God as so perfect that they operate always to work out His will—without the necessity of special interference on His part —than to see His hand directly operative in all th' phenomena of the universe.

CHAPTER X

OTHER SUNS THAN OURS

WE are now to venture into regions where we shall no longer have clear lights to guide us. Tremendous as are the dimensions of the solar system, the widest sweep of the planetary orbits sinks into insignificance compared with the distances which separate from us even the nearest of the fixed stars. From beyond depths which the human mind is utterly unable to conceive there come to us the rays of light which myriads of those orbs are pouring forth, and it is from the lessons taught us by these light-rays that we are to form our ideas concerning the nature of the orbs which emit them. Very carefully and cautiously must we proceed, if we would avoid being led into vain imaginings. It will but mislead us to pass a single step beyond the path which is dimly lighted for us, and yet that path is so narrow and so obstructed with difficulties, that we find ourselves continually tempted to leave it, and to venture forward on the alluring and easy paths which speculation opens out on every hand around us.

(238)

And yet we may well remain content to listen only to the teachings of known facts. Even so restraining ourselves, we have in reality a wide and noble domain to explore. Facts which seem severally unimportant are found, when considered as parts of a grand whole, to indicate relations so impressive and so interesting, that the revelations of the telescope within the solar system are apt to seem commonplace beside them. We have, in fact, to consider no longer the structure of a system—the architecture of the universe is our theme.

Let us examine carefully the evidence which science has gathered together for us, endeavoring at each step to gain the full amount of knowledge the several facts involve, while, at the same time, cautiously refraining from any attempt to overstep the bounds indicated by our evidence.

In the first place, let us consider what may be learned from the analogy of the solar system. The study is an inviting one, since the discoveries on which we are to found our views have been made so recently, that the subject has all the charm of novelty and freshness, while it involves the consideration of the soundest and most instructive mode of pursuing our researches.

We have seen in the solar system a variety and complexity of structure such as, half a century ago, few astronomers would have thought of ascribing to it. When Sir William Herschel began that noble series of researches amid the sidereal depths by which his name has been rendered illustrious, he saw in

the solar system a scheme very different indeed from
that which is presented to our contemplation.   He
beheld a vast central body, surrounded by a limited
number of orbs, some of which were the centres of
subordinate schemes of greater or less extent.   When
we have added the ring of Saturn as the only formation differing from planets and satellites in character,
and the comets few and far between, which seemed
rather accidental tributaries of the sun than regular
members of his family, we have considered all the
features which the solar system, as known in Sir
William Herschel's day, presented to the contemplation of astronomers.

With us it is very different.   We see that there
exists within the solar system a variety of size and
structure, of motion, arrangement, and aggregation,
which is already inconceivable, and yet doubtless
but faintly shadows forth the real complexity and
richness of the scheme swayed by our sun.   Perhaps
it is in considering the solar system in the particular
light in which, in this treatise, I have had occasion
to present it, that this wonderful variety of conformation is made most strikingly apparent.   But, apart
from all speculative theories, there can be no doubt
that the solar system presents to us a subject of
study amazing in itself, but most amazing when we
regard it as supplying the analogies which are to
guide us in forming our views respecting the sidereal system.   Besides the family of planets circling
round the sun, besides the system of dependent orbs
which circle round the planets, we see a zone in

which independent planets circle by hundreds, perhaps even by myriads, round the solar orb; we see the ring of Saturn composed of thousands of tiny bodies; we see the meteoric systems in countless hosts; we see the comets of our scheme in millions on millions; and less certainly, but still not indistinctly, we recognize the existence of a multitude of new and hitherto unsuspected forms of matter within the circle of our sun's attraction.

What opinion, then, are we to form—even here, at the very outset of our inquiry—respecting the sidereal scheme of which our sun forms but a unit? Surely it would be to lose sight of the significant lesson taught us by the solar system, it would be to forget how sure and safe a guide the greatest of modern astronomers found in the teachings of analogy, to adopt the same view now which that great astronomer adopted a century ago. If, viewing the solar system as consisting of discrete orbs, comparable one with another in size, and distributed not without a certain uniformity around their ruling centre, Sir William Herschel held that the sidereal scheme presented somewhat similar relations, surely *we*, who know certainly that the solar system is constituted so differently, must adopt a far different view of the sidereal scheme also.

Let us remember that there is here—so far as our respect and admiration for Sir William Herschel are concerned—a choice between two courses. Assuming, as indeed is just, that the views of our great men are not rashly to be thrown on one side, we have to choose whether we would rather abandon the views which Sir William Herschel formed about *facts*, or the views which he formed about *principles*. If we accept his opinion (or rather, after all, his mere suggestion) that the stars are tolerably uniform in magnitude and distribution, we must abandon the analogy of the solar system. If, on the contrary, we accept Sir William Herschel's often-expressed opinion that, in theorizing about the unknown, there can be no safer guide than the analogy of known facts, we must abandon the view (which seemed to him but probable) that the stars are distributed with tolerable uniformity throughout our galaxy, and are comparable *inter se* in magnitude and splendor.

There can be no doubt which course is preferable. We know certainly that Sir William Herschel was often mistaken, as all men must be, in matters of fact; while we know with equal certainty that he owed the marvellous success with which he theorized, to his adoption of the principle that analogy is the chief and the best guide for the student of astronomy.

We are compelled, then, in our very respect and admiration for the greatest astronomer of modern times, to regard the constitution of the sidereal system as, in all probability, very different from what he imagined.

We must be prepared to expect an infinite variety of figure, of structure, of motion, and of aggregation throughout the galactic scheme. If some orbs within that scheme seem probably to be suns like our own, **we must not be** surprised to find others which are probably far larger or far smaller. We may look for objects differing as much from the suns of the sidereal system as the asteroidal zone differs from Saturn or from Jupiter. So that, if we should recognize evidence of the existence of clusters of minute stars —a whole cluster, perhaps, not equalling in real importance the least of the suns of the system—we may accept that evidence without any scruples suggested by the improbability of the conclusion to which it points. Again, we may expect to find schemes within the sidereal system, differing as much from discrete stars or star-clusters as the rings of Saturn differ from the primary planets or from the asteroidal zone. So that, if we should recognize evidence of the existence of relatively minute clusters, whose components are either so small or so closely aggregated as not to be separately visible even in our most powerful telescopes, this evidence may fairly be accepted as accordant with the only analogy we have for our guidance. Yet once more: we may look for systems differing as much from all ordinary star-clusters as the eccentric and far-reaching meteor-systems differ from the symmetrical rings of Saturn. So that, if we should find evidence of strange schemes within the sidereal system, schemes presenting every *bizarre* variety of figure, with strange complexities of spiral whorls or outlying branches, losing themselves, as it were, in the depths toward which they seem to extend—this also need not surprise us: we need not conclude that *here*, at any rate, we are looking beyond the bounds of the sidereal system, and gazing upon external galaxies, for the analogy we have chosen for our guidance teaches us that such structures were to be expected within the scheme of which our sun is a component. And, finally, if we should find reason to assure ourselves that there are objects in the depths of space whose very substance and constitution are different from those of all other objects within the sidereal system, we need by no means believe that the objects thus singularly constituted belong to, or form, external systems. For the millions on millions of comets which form part and parcel of the solar system present a precisely analogous difference of structure, as compared with the other members of that system.

Having thus replaced the erroneous analogies to which—through no fault of his own—Sir William Herschel was led to look for guidance, by the more trustworthy analogies which the recent progress of astronomy has afforded for our instruction, we may proceed to consider the direct evidence we have respecting the constitution of our galaxy.

In the first place, let us examine the evidence which points to the dimensions of the sidereal system.

That the nearest members of the system lie at enormous distances from us is proved by the fact that, as the earth sweeps on her vast orbit round the sun, no appreciable change is observed in the configuration of the star-groups. That a circle having a diameter of more than one hundred and eighty millions of miles should be swept out year by year

as the earth traverses her orbit, and yet that the surrounding stars should exhibit no change of place, is
at once the most striking and the simplest evidence
we have of the enormous scale on which the sidereal
system is constructed. And yet this first obvious
fact sinks almost into insignificance when we regard
thoughtfully the teaching of modern instrumental
astronomy. There might be a real shifting of apparent position which yet the unaided eye would fail
to detect, and such a change would indicate distances
so enormous that the mind fails altogether to conceive their real significance. But the exact instruments of modern times would exhibit a change of
place infinitely more minute than any which the unaided eye could recognize. If a star shifted by so
much as the ten-thousandth part of the moon's apparent diameter, modern astronomers could assure
themselves of the change of place. And when we
remember that in precisely the same proportion that
we increase the exactitude of instrumental observation we increase also the significance of the stars'
apparent fixity of position, it will be seen at once
how astounding is the lesson conveyed by the fact
that all but a very few indeed of the stars remain
absolutely unaffected—even under the most powerful
instrumental examination—by the enormous range of
the earth's orbital motion.

We can roughly estimate the distances of the few
stars which are thus affected, and thence—on the
hypothesis that the intrinsic brilliancy of their light
is the same as the sun's—we may form some idea of

their dimensions. I shall, however, only apply this process, in detail, to a single case, because my present object is rather to indicate in a general way the scale on which the sidereal system is constructed, than to enter at length on the more exact details which find their place in ordinary treatises on astronomy.

The star Alpha Centauri is one of the brightest in the heavens, Sirius and Canopus alone surpassing it in splendor. But it is not its exceptional brilliancy alone which led astronomers to regard it as likely to afford evidence of an apparent change of place corresponding to the earth's real change of place as she sweeps round her orbit. Of course, the brightest stars are presumably the nearest; but there is another indication of proximity at least equally important. The so-called fixed stars are in reality slowly moving onward on definite courses— slowly, that is, in appearance, though in reality their motions are doubtless inconceivably rapid. Now, these motions, the *proper motions* of the stars, as they are called, are as yet very little understood. We know only that the whole of the galactic system is astir with life, but whither the orbs are severally tending we are not yet able to say. Nor do we know what portion of the stellar motions may be due to the undoubted proper motion of our own sun through space. This, however, may be regarded as certain, that, until we know something respecting the laws which regulate the stellar movements, we must regard the magnitude of a star's motion as probably an indication of relative proximity. Precisely as a man walking at a great distance from us appears to move much more slowly than one who is walking at the same rate close by, so the apparent rate of a star's motion is diminished in proportion to the star's distance from us. When, therefore, it was found that the star Alpha Centauri is moving more rapidly than other stars, this fact, combined with the great lustre of the star, led astronomers to suspect that it must be comparatively near to us.

Observations, made to determine whether the star shows any sign of an annual change of place corresponding to the earth's annual orbital motion, were rewarded by the detection of a very appreciable displacement. In fact, owing to the motion of the earth, each year, in a nearly circular orbit one hundred and eighty million miles in diameter, the star Alpha Centauri appears to trace out each year a minute oval path on the celestial sphere, the greater axis of the oval being equal in length to about $\frac{1}{100}$th part of the moon's apparent diameter.[1]

It follows from this that, in round numbers, the distance of Alpha Centauri from us is about twenty millions of millions of miles. The distance of the earth from the sun shrinks into insignificance beside this enormous gap. Even Neptune, though circling round the sun at a distance three hundred times

---

[1] It hardly need be mentioned, perhaps, that this motion being super-added to the star's more considerable proper motion, the path which the star seems really to follow is a looped one, the size of each loop being small in comparison with the distance between successive loops.

vaster than that which separates us from that luminary, is yet relatively so much nearer than Alpha Centauri, that a sun filling the whole orbit of Neptune would appear, as seen from that star, but about one-ninth as large as the sun appears to us.

Now let us consider what dimensions we may assign to Alpha Centauri, on the assumption that the surface of this star emits a light as brilliant as that which proceeds from the photosphere of our own sun. We must not neglect the consideration that the star is double—the companion emitting perhaps about one-sixteenth as much light as the primary.[1] The distance of Alpha Centauri is equal to about two hundred and thirty thousand times that which separates us from the sun. Therefore, if removed to the star's distance, the sun would shine with only $\frac{1}{52,900,000,000}$th part of his present brilliancy. Now, according to the most careful estimates of the brilliancy of Alpha Centauri, the light we receive from that star is about $\frac{1}{16,950,000,000}$th of that we receive from the sun.[2] It follows, therefore, that the star emits about three times as much light as the sun; and therefore, so far as the emission of light is a criterion of size, the star may be regarded as considerably larger than our own sun. In fact, reducing the

[1] Sir John Herschel, observing the star with his twenty-foot reflector, thought the secondary brighter than it is usually considered. I cannot but think that, for a comparison of this sort, smaller telescopes may more safely be trusted.

[2] This estimate is founded on Sir John Herschel's comparison between the light of the star and that of the full moon, and Zöllner's comparison between the light of the full moon and that of the sun.

total light of the pair by one-sixteenth, we find that
the primary must still emit about three times as
much light as the sun, and therefore the diameter
of the star, as thus estimated, would appear to
exceed our sun's in the proportion of about seventeen to ten.

We have here, then, clear and decisive evidence
in favor of the view that among the fixed stars there
are orbs which may be regarded as veritable suns,
worthy to be the ruling centres of schemes as noble
as the solar system. For we know quite certainly
that the greater number of the first-magnitude stars
are very much further from us than Alpha Centauri,
with which, however, they are fairly comparable in
brilliancy: so that they may be regarded as for the
most part at least equal to that star in size and mass.
Sirius and Canopus, indeed, must far surpass Alpha
Centauri. The latter, though more than thrice as
bright, exhibits no appreciable change of position
as the earth circles round the sun. Sirius, which is
more than four times brighter than Alpha Centauri,
shows an annual change of position which certainly
does not exceed one-fourth of that star's. It is
therefore four times further from us than Alpha
Centauri, and, did it emit no greater amount of
light, would appear to shine with but one-sixteenth
of that star's lustre. As in reality it is four times
as bright, the real amount of light it emits must
exceed that of Alpha Centauri no less than sixty-
four times, and that of our own sun no less than one
hundred and ninety-two times. So that, judged from

this indication alone, the diameter of Sirius may be held to exceed that of our sun in the proportion of about fourteen to one, an estimate which assigns to Sirius a diameter of nearly twelve million miles, and a volume two thousand six hundred and eighty-eight times as large as the sun's.

But, on the other hand, still confining our attention to this method of estimating magnitude, we find reason for believing that many of the visible stars must fall far short of our sun in magnitude. The sixth-magnitude double star, 61 Cygni, has been found to be nearer to us than Sirius, and about three times as far from us as Alpha Centauri. Now, we may assume that each component sends us about one-hundredth part of the light we receive from Alpha Centauri; it follows that the latter star, if removed to the distance at which 61 Cygni lies from us (when its light would of course be diminished to one-ninth of its present value), would outshine either component of that double star more than eleven times; hence (on the assumption that brightness is a fair measure of real dimensions), each component has a diameter less than one-third that of Alpha Centauri. We may roughly estimate the volume of each at about $\frac{1}{30}$th of that of the latter star. So that, remembering what has already been shown respecting the relation between Alpha Centauri and our sun, the two suns which form the double star 61 Cygni would each have a diameter equal to about $\frac{13}{16}$ths of the sun's, and a volume equal to about $\frac{4}{7}$ths. The sum of their volumes would be therefore about one-

third of his; and it will presently appear that a perfectly distinct mode of estimation tends to show that
the sum of their masses bears about the same proportion to the sun's mass.

But here at once we have evidence that there is
a very wide range of magnitude among the fixed
stars. We have seen reason to believe that Sirius is
twenty-six hundred and eighty-eight times as large
as the sun, while each of the suns forming the
double star 61 Cygni would appear to have a volume less than one-fifth of our sun's, and therefore
less than $\frac{1}{13500}$th of the volume of Sirius. So that,
by considering only three cases, we have found tolerably clear evidence of a range of variety in volume, reminding us forcibly of that which we recognize in the solar system. We cannot suppose that
these three cases, which have been selected at random—so far as the question of volume is concerned
—indicate anything like the real limits within which
the fixed stars differ in magnitude. So that we may
confidently accept, as the most probable conclusion
from the evidence before us, that the range of real
magnitude among the fixed stars is very far greater
than Sir W. Herschel was led to anticipate, when,
nearly a century ago, he began his researches into
the sidereal system.

But it is not sufficient that we should thus form
an estimate of the nature of the fixed stars, from the
amount of light they send to us. It is desirable—
and fortunately it is practicable—to obtain information as to the absolute mass or weight of some of

the fixed stars, and further to ascertain of what substances they may be composed, and in what condition those substances may exist. Mere lights, however glorious, or however wide the sphere within
which they displayed their splendors, would not be
fit to sway the motions of orbs resembling those
which circle around our sun. Nor would such
lights serve to indicate to the astronomer that, out
yonder, myriads of millions of miles beyond the extreme limits of the solar system, there exist materials
suited to form the substance of worlds resembling our
own.

It seems a strange circumstance that astronomers
should be able to form a more exact and trustworthy
estimate of the weight of certain fixed stars than they
can hope to form respecting the volume of any of
those bodies. Let us consider what evidence we have
on this point.

I have spoken of the star 61 Cygni as a double
star. The smaller star shows very clear indications
of orbital motion around its primary. That the two
are associated together, and not merely seen, as it
were by an accident, nearly in the same line of
view, is indeed certain, because that peculiarly large
proper motion already referred to is shared in by
both. But many stars may be physically associated,
and yet the distance really separating them may
enormously exceed that by which they seem to be
separated—since the line joining them is not necessarily square to the line of sight. The components
of the star 61 Cygni have been carefully watched,

however, and their motions show that they are circling around each other. The distance separating
them is probably about half as large again as the
distance of Neptune from the sun.

The period of revolution appears to be about five
hundred and twenty years, which is more than three
times as great as the period of Neptune. Now, we
know that a planet placed at a distance from the sun
equal to that which separates the components of 61
Cygni, would occupy a much less period than five
hundred and twenty years in completing a revolution; in fact, its period would be about three hundred years. Hence it follows that the components
of 61 Cygni are attracted together less forcibly than
Neptune is attracted toward the sun, and therefore
that the sum of their masses must be less than the
sun's mass. It is easy to compute the actual proportion, and we find accordingly that the two components of 61 Cygni, taken together, weigh about
one-third as much as our sun.[1]

The star Alpha Centauri is also a binary system,
and, though it has not been so systematically observed as 61 Cygni, some astronomers believe that
its period has been even more satisfactorily determined. Indeed, there are peculiarities in the motion of 61 Cygni, which, without throwing doubt on
the general conclusions deduced above, yet suggest

---

[1] It may easily be shown that, if a pair of bodies, circling around each
other at a certain distance, take a certain time T in effecting a revolution,
while another pair at the same distance take a time t, the former pair,
taken together, have a weight which bears to the weight of the latter pair
the ratio of t^2 to T^2.

that a third (probably opaque) orb affects the motions of the other two. From a careful comparison of all the observations made in recent times on Alpha Centauri, Mr. Hind has assigned to the components a period of revolution of about eighty-one years, and a mean distance of 13.6 seconds of arc, corresponding to a real distance exceeding the earth's distance from the sun some fifteen times. Since a planet placed at this distance from the sun would occupy less than sixty years in completing a revolution around that body, it follows that the mass of the two components of Alpha Centauri must be less than that of the sun. This result (if the data be considered trustworthy) would indicate a considerable difference between the condition of the star and that of our sun; for we have seen that the star gives out much more light than the sun. However, I believe that many years must elapse before we can regard the period of Alpha Centauri as satisfactorily determined.

Still, we have conclusive evidence in this case, as in that of the star 61 Cygni, that the component stars are really bodies of enormous weight, and consequently well fitted to sway the motions of families of planets. We conclude, therefore, that the fixed stars generally are *suns*, not mere *lights;* and, further, we are led to believe that there must be a general similarity in the conditions under which these bodies and our own sun emit light. And thus we are led to recognize other stars also—though as yet unweighed—as massive orbs, not merely supplying light to other worlds travelling around them, but regulating by their attractive influences the orbital motions of their dependent worlds.

But we owe to the revelations of the spectroscope the complete proof of these matters, besides evidence on other and equally interesting points.

It had long been known that the spectra of the fixed stars present a general resemblance to the solar spectrum, though of course very much fainter, and that dark lines can be seen in these spectra, some of which correspond with those in the sun's spectrum, while others seem to be new. So soon as the great discovery effected by Kirchhoff had been announced, it was seen at once that these dark lines in the stellar spectra afford the means of determining the constitution of the stars. It was only necessary that these lines should be identified by their correspondence with the lines belonging to known elements, in order to prove that these elements exist in the substance of the star. But, although the principle on which researches were to be conducted was sufficiently simple, many difficulties had to be encountered. Indeed, the attempts made by Airy, Secchi, and Rutherford, to solve the problem of determining the constitution of the stars by means of spectroscopic analysis, were unsuccessful; and it was not until Professor Miller and Mr. Huggins commenced their famous series of researches that the problem can be said to have been fairly mastered.

Even in the hands of these eminent physicists the work was difficult, and its progress tedious. The

weather necessary for the successful prosecution of
so delicate a method of inquiry does not often prevail in our variable climate.   The comparison between the dark lines in the stellar spectra and the
bright lines belonging to various elements was not
only a delicate and laborious task, but was singularly painful to the eyes.   And other difficulties, into
which I have not space to enter here, had to be
encountered and overcome.

But, undeterred by these difficulties, the two
physicists persevered in their researches, and were
rewarded by results so interesting and important that
their discovery may be said to constitute the most
remarkable era in the history of sidereal research
since the completion of the star-gaugings of the elder
Herschel.

Two bright stars, Betelgeux, the leading brilliant
of Orion, and Aldebaran, the chief star of Taurus,
were examined with special care.   Mr. Huggins remarks that the spectra of these stars are as rich in
lines as the solar spectrum itself.   The places of no
less than eighty lines in the spectrum of Betelgeux
were accurately measured, while as many as seventy
lines had their places assigned to them in the spectrum of Aldebaran.

With respect to the former spectrum, Mr. Huggins remarks that it is most complex and remarkable.
"Strong groups of lines are visible, especially in the
red, the green, and the blue portions," a peculiarity, it may be remarked in passing, which serves to
account for the well-marked orange-color of this star.

Now, here already we have very decided evidence as to the nature of the star; since the very fact that its spectrum presents the same general appearance as the solar spectrum, proves conclusively that the star is an incandescent body, whose light comes to us through certain vapors corresponding to those which surround the sun. Nor should we be able to regard the star as other than a sun, even though none of the elements known to us should appear to be present in its substance, or in the vapors surrounding it. For, clearly, we have no reason for believing that worlds can be formed out of those elements only with which we are acquainted, unless we find, as we proceed, that those elements actually do compose the suns which form the sidereal system. Of course, if this shall appear to be the case, our conclusions respecting the nature of the stars will be very much strengthened.

Now, when Professor Miller and Mr. Huggins compared the lines in the spectrum of Betelgeux with the bright lines of certain terrestrial elements, they found that some of these elements do actually exist in the vaporous envelope of the stars. Thus, sodium, magnesium, calcium, iron, and bismuth, are present in Betelgeux. The lines of hydrogen, which are so well marked in the solar spectrum, are not seen in the spectrum of Betelgeux. We are not to conclude from this that hydrogen does not exist in the composition of the star. We know that certain parts of the solar disk, when examined with the spectroscope, do not at all times exhibit the hydrogen lines, or may even present them as bright instead of dark lines. It may well be that in Betelgeux hydrogen exists under such conditions that the amount of light it sends forth is nearly equivalent to the amount it absorbs, in which case its characteristic lines would not be easily discernible. In fact, it is important to notice generally, that, while there can be no mistaking the positive evidence afforded by the spectroscope as to the existence of any element in sun or star, the negative evidence supplied by the absence of particular lines is not to be certainly relied upon.

In the case of Aldebaran the two physicists were able to establish the existence of sodium, magnesium, hydrogen, calcium, iron, bismuth, tellurium, antimony, and mercury, in the vapors surrounding the star.

Besides these stars, fifty others were examined. The brilliant Sirius exhibits a spectrum of great beauty, though the low altitude which this star attains in our latitudes rendered the observation of the finer lines exceedingly difficult. But the two physicists were able to show that sodium, magnesium, hydrogen, and probably iron, exist in this gigantic sun.

All the stars examined exhibit spectra crossed by numerous lines; and, in a great number of the spectra, lines belonging to known terrestrial elements were detected.

And now let us consider the general bearing of these interesting discoveries.

In the first place, we are forced to recognize in the stars *real suns*, not mere lights. Doubtless Dr.

Whewell did well in pointing out that astronomers had no right to regard the stars as suns, until they had some evidence that these orbs resemble the sun in other respects than in size, mass, or luminosity. And as in his day it appeared altogether unlikely that such evidence should be obtained, a real limit seemed placed to the speculations men might form as to the existence of other planetary systems besides those which circle around the sun.

But now we have precisely that evidence which Whewell required. We see that the stars are constituted in the same general way as the sun, and that, further, they even contain elements identical with those which exist in his substance. There is not indeed in every case, perhaps there may not be in any case, an exact identity of composition between star and sun, or between star and star. But this was no more to have been looked for than an exact identity of physical habitudes among the members of the solar system. That general resemblance of structure which indicates a general resemblance in the purposes which the celestial bodies are intended to subserve, is undoubtedly evident, when we compare the stars either with our sun or with each other.

I have already spoken of the conclusions to be drawn from the existence of the same materials in the substance of the sun that exist around us on this earth. I have shown that we are compelled to regard this general resemblance of structure as sufficient to prove that the other planets resemble the earth, since we have no reason to believe that our earth bears an exceptionally close resemblance to the sun as respects the elements of which she is composed.

Since, then, we have reason to believe that all the planets which circle around the sun are constituted of the same materials which exist in his substance, though these materials are not necessarily nor probably combined in the same proportions throughout the solar system, we have every reason which analogy can give us for believing that the planets circling around Betelgeux or Aldebaran are constituted of the same materials which exist in the substance of their central luminary.

Thus we are led to a number of interesting conclusions even respecting orbs which no telescope that man can construct is likely to reveal to his scrutiny. The existence of such elements as sodium or calcium in those other worlds suggests the probable existence of the familiar compounds of these metals—soda, salt, lime, and so on. Again, the existence of iron and other metals of the same class carries our minds to the various useful purposes which these metals are made to subserve on the earth. We are at once invited to recognize that the orbs circling around those distant suns are not meant merely to be the abode of life, but that intelligent creatures, capable of applying these metals to useful purposes, must exist in those worlds. We need not conclude, indeed, that at the present moment every one of those worlds is peopled with intelligent beings, because we have good reason for believing that throughout an enormous proportion of the time during which our earth has existed as a world no intelligent use has been made of the supplies of metal existing in her substance. But that at some time or other those worlds have been or will be the abode of intelligent creatures seems to be a conclusion very fairly deducible from what we now know of their probable structure.

But, secondly, apart from the information afforded by the spectroscope respecting the materials of which the stars are composed, the nature of the stellar spectra serves to prove most conclusively that the stars, besides supplying light to the worlds which circle around them, radiate heat also to them. Even if we were not certain that elements which are only vaporized at a very high temperature exist in the vaporous envelopes of the stars, yet the very nature of the light sent out by the stars indicates that these orbs are incandescent through intensity of heat. When we find that the spectrum of a planet's light resembles the solar spectrum, we do not indeed conclude that the planet is as intensely heated as the sun, because we know that the planets are not self-luminous. But, in the case of self-luminous bodies like the stars, we can conclude from the very nature of their spectra that these orbs are intensely heated. Of course we are rendered absolutely certain of this when we find that iron and other metals exist in the form of vapor in the stellar atmospheres.

The vast supplies of heat thus emitted by the stars not only suggest the conclusion that there must be worlds around these orbs for which those heat-supplies are intended, but point to the existence in

those worlds of the various forms of force into which
heat may be transmuted.   We know that the sun's
heat poured upon our earth is stored up in vegetable
and animal forms of life; is present in all the phenomena of Nature—in winds, and clouds, and rain,
in thunder and lightning, storm and hail; and that
even the works of man are performed by virtue of
the solar heat-supplies.   Thus the fact, that the stars
send forth heat to the worlds which circle around
them, suggests at once the thought that on those
worlds there must exist vegetable and animal forms
of life; that natural phenomena, such as we are
familiar with as due to the solar heat, must be produced in those worlds by the heat of their central
sun; and that works such as those which man under-
takes on earth—works in which intelligent creatures
use Nature's powers to master Nature to their purposes—must go on in the worlds which circle around
Aldebaran and Betelgeux, around Vega, Capella, and
the blazing Sirius.

Recently it has even been found possible to render the stellar heat sensible to terrestrial observation,
by methods which need not here be inquired into.
Nay, the task of measuring the amount of heat received from certain stars has not been thought too
difficult.   Mr. Stone, making use of the powers of
the great equatorial of the Greenwich Observatory,
and ingeniously overcoming the numerous difficulties
which exist in a research of such exceeding delicacy,
has arrived at the conclusion that Arcturus sends us
about as much heat as would be received from a

three-inch cube full of boiling water, and placed at
a distance of three hundred and eighty-three yards.
Vega, which shines, according to Sir J. Herschel,
with about two-thirds the light of Arcturus, gives
out about the same proportionate amount of heat.[1]
But in other instances the heat-giving power of a
star has not been found proportional to the amount
of light it emits.

The variation of many fixed stars in lustre at
once forms a new bond of association between the
stars and the sun—which we have seen to be in reality a variable star—and suggests interesting inquiries
as to the existence of variation in the emission of
heat. Some of the stellar variations of light are so
much more marked than those noticed in the case
of our own sun that we can scarcely conceive how
creatures, resembling any with which we are acquainted, could endure the effects of corresponding
important variations of heat; nay, in some instances

---

[1] Although these results cannot yet be regarded as numerically exact,
it may be interesting to consider the amount of heat given out by Arcturus
in relation to the light sent us by this star, the more so as this star seems
(from the nature of its spectrum) to resemble the sun very closely in constitution.

The light sent to us by Arcturus is equal to about three-fourths of
that supplied by Alpha Centauri, or about $\frac{1}{21,000,000,000}$th part of the light we
receive from the sun. Now, Mr. Stone estimates the direct heating effect
of Arcturus at $0°.00,000,127$ Fahrenheit, making due allowance for the
effect of the object-glass in concentrating and absorbing the heat. It will
be seen at once that, according to this estimate, the heating power of
Arcturus bears a very much greater proportion to that of the sun than
the respective light-giving powers of these luminaries bear to each other.
This seems to throw some doubt on the correctness of the estimate, either
of the light-giving or of the heat-giving power of the star.

we seem compelled to withhold our belief in the
existence of habitable systems around certain fixed
stars. The star Eta Argûs, for example, which sometimes blazes out with a light surpassing that of any
of the stars in the northern hemisphere, while at
other times it falls to the sixth magnitude, can
hardly be regarded as fit to be the centre of a
system of worlds. I pass over such variable stars
as the one which recently blazed out in the Northern Crown, because in a case of this sort the star
may be regarded as really a small orb, and its sudden lustre as due to some exceptional occurrence,
leading (as the spectrum of the star seemed to show)
to a temporary conflagration. But Eta Argûs and
Mira Ceti seem to belong to a different category altogether, since it is probable as respects the former,
and certain as respects the latter, that their appearance as stars of the leading magnitudes is not accidental, but part of a systematic series of changes.

It remains only to be mentioned that, besides
light and heat, the stars emit actinic rays. This is
proved decisively by the fact that the stars can be
made to photograph themselves. It has been found,
however, that the actinic power of a star, like its
heat-giving power, is not by any means proportional
to the star's light. So that in this respect, as in the
material constitution of the stars, we find specific
varieties even amid those very features which indicate most strikingly the general resemblance which
exists between the suns constituting the sidereal
system.

To sum up what we have learned so far from the study of the starry heavens—we see that, besides our sun, there are myriads of other suns in the immensity of space; that these suns are large and massive bodies, capable of swaying by their attraction systems of worlds as important as those which circle around the sun; that these suns are formed of elements similar to those which constitute our own sun, so that the worlds which circle round them may be regarded as in all probability similar in constitution to this earth; and that from those suns all the forms of force which we know to be necessary to the existence of organized beings on our earth are abundantly emitted. Is it not reasonable to conclude that these suns have not been made in vain? If thoughtful men have reasoned rightly in supposing that the light and heat poured out by the sun upon the planets which circle around him are not wasted—in the case of all the planets except our small earth—by being shed where no forms of life can profit by those abundant supplies, surely the argument is a million-fold stronger in the case of the fixed stars. Though here we cannot, as in the case of the solar system, actually see the worlds about which we speculate, yet the mind presents them clearly before us, various in size, various in structure, infinitely various in their physical condition and habitudes, but alike in this, that each is peopled by creatures perfectly adapted to the circumstances surrounding them, and that each exhibits, in the clearest and most striking manner, the wisdom and beneficence of the Almighty

CHAPTER XI

OF MINOR STARS, AND OF THE DISTRIBUTION OF
STARS IN SPACE

IT has been so long a received opinion that a general uniformity of magnitude and distribution characterizes the stellar system that it is with some diffidence I venture to express a different view. And here let me not be misunderstood. I am fully sensible that it is only in certain popular treatises of astronomy that a belief in anything like a real uniformity of structure in the sidereal system is attributed to astronomers of authority. It is not any such imaginary theory that I have now to deal with, however, but with opinions which have found a place in the works of astronomers from whom I very unwillingly differ.

I propose to exhibit the reasons which have led me to believe that, so far from knowing the real figure of the sidereal system, astronomers have not been able to penetrate to its limits in *any* direction; that leading stars, such as those discussed in the preceding chapter, are distributed throughout space to the very furthest limits and beyond the very furthest limits that our most powerful telescopes can attain to;

(266)

that the stars are arranged in groups and clustering aggregations, in streams and whorls and spirals, in a manner altogether too complex for us to hope to interpret; and that in these aggregations stars of all degrees of real magnitude are mixed up, from suns as large as Sirius down to orbs which may be smaller than any of the primary planets of the solar system.

Now let us consider step by step the evidence we have on these points.

We know, from the existence of double, triple, and multiple stars, in which the components are often very unequal in splendor, that combinations of stars exist in which one or two may be suns like our own, while the rest, or some of the rest, are relatively minute. This, however, has of course long been known; and it is only as a preliminary step in the investigation that I here advance so trite an instance.

Next let us consider such star-clusters as contain orbs of the eighth or ninth magnitude, besides a multitude of minute stars. These clusters must of course be regarded as lying within the sidereal system, since no external galaxies could reasonably be supposed to contain orbs so infinitely transcending even Sirius in magnitude as to shine, from beyond the enormous gap separating us from such galaxies, with a light exceeding that derived from many stars within the sidereal system. Now, regarding these clusters as forming part and parcel of the sidereal system, we find in the existence of multitudes of minute orbs within their range a proof that diversity of magnitude in schemes of associated stars is to be regarded as a feature of certain parts, at any rate, of our galaxy; and we shall therefore be the less surprised if we should find reason for believing that it is a *characteristic peculiarity* of the galactic system.

Now, with regard to the nebulæ (resolvable and irresolvable), and their claim to be regarded as external galaxies, I shall have much to say further on; but I may remark, in passing, that we have precisely the same reasons for believing that many of these objects lie within the range of the solar system as have been already considered in the case of star-clusters. Their component stars, to be visible at all, *must* fall within the range of distance which astronomers have assigned to the boundaries of the galaxy, since some stars even within that range cease to be separately visible in the most powerful telescopes man has yet constructed. So that when in these objects we see a few or many distinct stars, and a mass of nebulous light which we judge to proceed from an indefinitely large number of minute stars, we again have very decided evidence of the fact that in one and the same region of the sidereal system there may exist leading stars (so to speak) and innumerable stars relatively minute.

With considerations such as these (and I might add many others) to guide us, let us proceed to consider the teachings of the Milky Way itself, that we may see whether that wonderful zone indeed represents, as has been thought, the sidereal system itself, or only an aggregation of minute orbs altogether insignificant, separately, in comparison with our sun or Sirius, Aldebaran or Betelgeux, Vega or Arcturus.

The star-gauging of Sir W. Herschel, interpreted according to his hypothesis of stellar distribution, pointed to an extension of the Milky Way laterally to a distance exceeding some eighty times that which separates us from the first-magnitude stars. So that, regarding sixth-magnitude stars as on the average about ten times as far from us as those of the first magnitude (the usual estimate), we see that the outer-most parts of the galaxy must lie (according to Sir W. Herschel's theory) about eight times as far from us as the sphere of the sixth-magnitude stars. Now, Sir John Herschel was led by his observations of the southern heavens to so far modify his father's theory as to describe the Milky Way as probably shaped like a flat ring, the stars down to the tenth magni-tude being in a sense dissociated from the ring, while he regarded the probable distance of the outer-most limits of the ring as seven hundred and fifty times instead of but eighty times the mean distance of the first-magnitude stars. This difference of opin-ion, it may be remarked, though obviously not sur-prising when we consider the enormous difficulty of the problem presented by the sidereal system, is yet sufficient to indicate the probability that an impor-tant error has been made in the hypothesis which underlies the accepted theories respecting the galaxy. But, be this as it may, in regarding the Milky Way as shaped like a flat ring (cloven through one half of its circumference) whose medial section resembles generally the space between the dark concentric circles in the accompanying figure (in which SB equals eight times SA), I have not adopted a structure

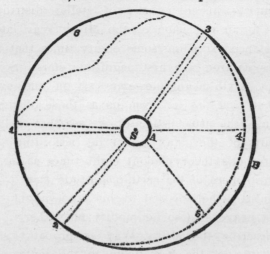

FIG. 2.—The Galactic Cloven Flat Ring (plan).

which *exaggerates* the difficulties presented by the disk or ring theory of the Milky Way. The cross-section would be somewhat as shown in Fig. 3.

Now, accepting this modified figure, as better according with the results of star-gauging than Sir **W.**

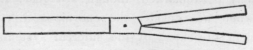

FIG. 3.—The Galactic Cloven Flat Ring (section).

Herschel's theory that the Milky Way forms a **cloven** disk, let us consider whether any peculiarities of the Milky Way seem to oppose themselves to this interpretation of its structure.

In the first place, then, there is a gap or rift extending right across the single part of the Milky Way in the constellation Argo; so that we must conceive that from S toward 1, in Fig. 2, the flat ring is broken through by some such rift as is indicated by the broken lines in that direction. Next there is, in the constellation Crux, a pear-shaped vacuity of considerable size, and bounded by well-defined edges; so that we must conceive that from S toward 2 (Fig. 2) the flat ring is tunnelled through by some such passage as is indicated by the dotted lines in that direction. A similar tunnelling, but of different cross-section, must exist in direction S 3 (as shown by the dotted lines) to account for the dark gap in the constellation Cygnus. Next, where the Milky Way is double, a large portion of one branch is discontinuous, so that the upper part of the double portion of the ring in Fig. 2 must be supposed removed between the broken lines from S to 4 and 5. Over the so-called double stream there are in places strange convolutions, in others numerous branching and interlacing streams, whose complexity indeed defies description; so that the portion 3 B 2 of the ring must be supposed corrugated in the strangest way, and further to throw out plane and curved sheets of stars presented tangentially toward S. Lastly, the single portion of the Milky Way is very faint indeed toward 6, so that here we must conceive its figure trenched in upon in the way indicated by the dot-and-peck line.

Thus, even without considering a multitude of

minuter peculiarities of structure, we are led to the
conclusion that the Milky Way, judged according to
the fundamental hypothesis of Sir W. Herschel, has
some such shape as I have endeavored to exhibit
in the accompanying figure. Although I have not
indicated here the corrugations of the ring, nor a
tithe of the various overlapping layers which would
be required to account for the appearance of the
Milky Way between Centaurus and Ophiuchus, yet
the deduced figure is by no means inviting in its

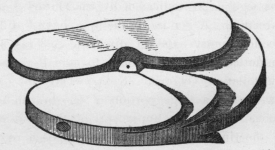

FIG. 4.—The Galactic Flat Ring, modified in accordance with
the observed peculiarities of the Milky Way.

simplicity. It is, however, absolutely certain that
the sidereal system, as far as its more densely aggregated star-regions are concerned, has some such figure as this, if we are to accept the principle of Sir
W. Herschel's star-gaugings.

Now, in turning our thoughts to the recognition
of a more simple explanation of observed appearances, it will be well that we should consider some
peculiarities of the Milky Way which we have not
yet attended to. In the first place, I would invite
attention to a peculiarity observed by Sir John Her-

schel in different parts of the galaxy—the fact, namely, that in places the edge of the Milky Way is quite sharply defined. One half of a telescopic field of view may be quite clear of stars, or show only a few straggling orbs, while the other half presents what has been called a "Milky Way field"— that is, a region profusely sprinkled with stars, the boundary between the two portions being well defined. When we see that a cluster of objects presents a well-defined edge, what conclusion do we draw as to the position of the object? Is it not in such a case absolutely certain that the distance of the cluster enormously exceeds the distance between its component parts—or, in other words, that the observer is far outside the cluster? Many instances will at once suggest themselves to the reader in illustration of this remark.

We conclude, then, that these portions of the Milky Way, at any rate, whether they be regarded as projections or nodules, are definite clustering aggregations very far removed from us. Other parts of the Milky Way *may* also be removed bodily, so to speak, to enormous distances, because a cluster which has not a definite edge may be as far removed as one which has; but certainly *those* portions are.

Next let us consider what opinion we may found on the existence of dark regions in the Milky Way; and here I refer not merely to such large and obvious vacuities as the coal-sack in Crux or the oval opening in Cygnus, but also to small openings, in which, though they occur even in rich regions of the

Milky Way, there is not, according to Sir W. Herschel's description, even a telescopic star to be seen.

Judged apart from preconceived opinions, such openings as these, according to all laws of probability, indicate that the portion of the Milky Way in which they occur has not a very great lateral extension. To return for a moment to Fig. 2, it will be seen at once that an aperture extending laterally through a star-system so shaped must have a particular direction and be perfectly straight in order to be visible to observers placed, as we are supposed to be, in the central opening. It is altogether improbable that one such opening should exist by accident, and absolutely impossible that many should.[1] We are forced therefore to infer that, instead of the enormous lateral extension assigned to the Milky Way, the galaxy has in these places certainly, and elsewhere probably, a lateral extension not greatly exceeding its depth.

It is further to be noted that the lucid stars over that zone of the heavens which is occupied by the galaxy show a very decided preference for the parts of that zone which are actually traversed by the Milky Way. For instance, we find no stars above the fifth magnitude, and very few of these, in the Coal-sacks, or in the rift which crosses the Milky

---

[1] Sir John Herschel has distinctly indicated this inference, as he has many other matters which make strongly against the received theory of the sidereal system. Nor is he unconscious of their bearing. Apparently unwilling at present to press them to their full extent, he is commonly satisfied by noting that they do not seem to accord with views he has elsewhere dwelt upon.

Way in Argo, or, again, in the space which lies between the two branches where the Milky Way is double. If this is an accident, it is a very extraordinary one, especially when it is remembered that the region where it occurs is the very part of the heavens where stars of all magnitudes may be expected to be most profusely distributed; that the spaces thus left vacant form no inconsiderable aliquot part of that zone; and that, according to the accepted theory, there is no reason for expecting any peculiarity of the sort.

Thus, again, setting aside preconceived opinions, and judging only according to the evidence, we seem led to regard the coincidence as not accidental, but as indicating that there really is a very close association between the bright stars and those small stars forming the milky light, which, according to the accepted theory, would lie so many times further from us.[1]

Now, if we have not been mistaken so far, it is very clear what views we are to form. If the Milky Way is to be, *first*, a clustering aggregation separated from us by an interval comparatively clear of small stars; *secondly*, so shaped that the cross-section of the stream is everywhere not far from a roughly circular figure; and, *thirdly*, associated very closely with the

---

[1] I may add that, in drawing the maps for my new star-atlas, I have been very much surprised to find how in many cases the position, nay, the very shape, of the Milky Way is indicated by the lucid stars which fall on its zone. Although my own views had led me to look for a peculiarity of the sort, it has been much more striking in its character than I had expected.

bright stars seen in the same field of view, then must
its structure be somewhat as shown in Fig. 5, in
which the disks represent lucid stars (very much
exaggerated of course in size), while the fine dot-
ting represents the spiral of relatively minute stars,
clustering along the spiral group of leading stars.
It will be seen at once how, to an observer placed
at S, the various features of the Milky Way can be

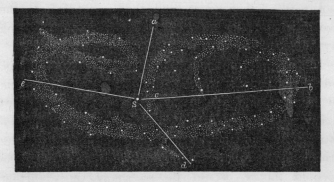

Fig. 5.—The Milky Way regarded as a Spiral.

accounted for by this figure. Toward *a* would lie
the gap in Argo; toward *b* two branches, one faint,
and in part evanescent through enormity of distance,
the other forming the brightest part of the spiral;
toward *d* the projection in Cepheus; toward *e* the
faint part of the Milky Way in Gemini and Mono-
ceros. The Coal-sacks would be simply accounted
for by conceiving that branches seen toward the
same general direction, but at different distances,
do not lie in the same general plane, and so may
appear to interlace upon the heavens. We are not
only justified in supposing this, but forced to do so

by the way in which the stream of milky light is observed to *meander* on its course athwart the heavens. The branching extensions serve very well to account for the appearance of the Milky Way between Centaurus and Ophiuchus, where the interlacing branches and the strange convolutions and clustering aggregations described by Sir John Herschel are chiefly gathered.

I would not have it understood, however, that I at all insist on the general shape of the spiral shown in Fig. 5. On the contrary, that curve is only one out of several which might fairly account for the observed appearance of the Milky Way; and I have often felt inclined to doubt whether a single spiral of this sort be in reality the best way of accounting for the observed appearance of the galactic zone. What I do insist upon as most obviously forced upon us by the evidence is, that (1) the apparent streams formed by the Milky Way upon the heavens indicate the existence of real streams in space; and (2) that the lucid stars seen on the stream are really associated with the telescopic stars which form, so to speak, the body of the stream. Whether that stream form a single spiral or several, or *whether, instead of spirals, there may not be a number of closed rings of small stars, placed at different distances from us, and lying in all directions round the medial plane of the galaxy, but more or less tilted to that plane (the sun not lying within any one of the rings),* are questions which can only be resolved by the systematic scrutiny of this wonderful zone.

The chief points to be noticed among the considerations flowing from these general views are these:

In the first place, the only marked difference between the stars of the leading magnitudes (say the
first ten) lying in the galactic zone, and those lying
without it, consists in the fact that the former are
associated with countless multitudes of smaller stars,
while the latter appear not to have such attendants,
or not so many of them. We shall see presently that
the extra-galactic stars *are* associated, and in a very
intimate manner, with groups of very minute stars—
of stars so minute indeed as not to be separately
discernible—so that astronomers have been led to
regard such groups as external galaxies. But, except
in one region, we do not find outside the galactic
zone any appearances reminding us of the aspect of
the Milky Way itself. In that region lie the two
Magellanic Clouds, resembling the Milky Way in
their general appearance, but seen when placed under
telescopic scrutiny to differ from it in this, that
among the minute stars which cause the milky light
are numbers of nebulæ, of classes not found commonly, if at all, in the galactic zone.

In the second place, we must conclude that uncounted millions of stars exist which are very minute indeed in comparison with those which we have
been led to regard as suns. That these relatively
minute orbs may be absolutely large—far larger, for
instance, than our own earth—may indeed be accepted as certain. But it is difficult to believe that
they subserve purposes similar to those of our own

sun. One cannot but see that orbs such as these would not have that permanence of character, as sources of heat-supply, which would seem to be necessary in the case of a real sun. We know, indeed, that among the small stars of the Milky Way there is a proneness to irregular variation which is not recognized, or is altogether exceptional, among the lucid stars. In the neighborhood of the Milky Way, with scarcely an exception, those temporary stars have blazed out which have formed a subject of such perplexity to the thoughtful astronomer. Under what conditions the small orbs in the Milky Way actually exist, whether clusters of them will eventually segregate from their neighbors to form suns, or whether, after long voyaging in spiral and contorted paths under the varying influences of the attractions of leading stars, these minute orbs will, for the most part, be forced to settle down as attendants round the major ones, it is as yet altogether impossible to judge. It may be that they bear the same sort of relation to the leading stars that certain cometic and meteoric families, referred to in Chapter IX., bear to the major planets of the solar system, not being in any case absolutely dependent on any large star, but yet returning in cycles which must be measured by millions of eons, to temporary dependence on one sun after another, until in the course of time, under the action of processes somewhat resembling those I have conceived to take place in the formation of the solar system, the conditions under which they move will have become so far altered as to lead to the breaking up of the Milky Way into distinct systems. Indeed, as Sir William Herschel was led by other considerations long since to point out, there are signs in parts of the Milky Way which would seem to indicate that several such systems have already reached an advanced stage of development.

But perhaps the most important conclusion deducible from the circumstances I have dwelt upon (assuming my interpretation of them to be in the main correct) is this, that we can no longer suppose we have in any direction pierced to the limits of the sidereal system. So long as a general approach to uniformity of distribution was understood to prevail within that system, there was a ready means of determining when the telescopist had reached in any given direction the limits of the system. To use the words of Professor Nichol, "When an eye is directed toward a prolonged bed of stars, there is no reason to fancy that it has reached the termination of that stratum so long as there appears, behind the luminaries which are individually seen, any milky or nebulous light; such light probably arising always from the blended rays of remoter masses. But, if, after struggling long with a nebulous ground, we obtain a telescope that gives us additional light with *a perfectly black sky*, we then have every reason the circumstances can furnish on behalf of the supposition that at length we have pierced through the stratum, a probability, indeed, which can be converted into certainty in only one way—viz., when no increase of orbs follows on the application of a still larger instrument." Sir John Herschel has expressed a similar view, and there can, indeed, be no doubt that, adopting the fundamental hypothesis on which accepted views are founded, the test above described is an absolutely certain one.

But, if, instead of penetrating further and further into space when "struggling long with a nebulous ground" (to use Professor Nichol's striking but somewhat incorrect expression), we have in reality only been searching with more and more minuteness within a definite cluster or stream of stars, we can no longer come to the conclusion he has insisted upon. We have reached the limits of minuteness which the stars of the cluster or stream attain to; we have learned perhaps all that we can learn about that cluster or stream; but we can no more be said to have reached the limits of the sidereal system in that direction than we can be said to have reached the outermost bounds of the universe in the direction of the cluster in Hercules, when that magnificent object has been thoroughly resolved with the telescope.

Here, then, if I have seemed to narrow the limits of the sidereal scheme by bringing the star-myriads of the Milky Way, which had been regarded as many times further from us than the lucid stars, into direct association with these luminaries, I make amends by pointing out that in all probability the limits of the sidereal system lie far beyond the range of the most powerful telescopes man has yet constructed. In fact, there is here a somewhat singular interchange of position between the new and the accepted theo-

ries. According to the views usually accepted, the
small stars in the Milky Way are really as large, on
the average, as the lucid stars, whereas, according
to my views, they are relatively minute. But, according to the accepted theories, the scattered stars of
very low magnitudes in the extra-galactic heavens
must be regarded as relatively minute, since it has
been rendered certain, according to those theories,
that the limits of the sidereal system are relatively
close in this direction, and we cannot suppose these
stars to lie beyond those limits (as they must do, if
really large). Now, according to my views, there is
nothing to prevent these minute stars from including
among their number orbs as vast as Sirius, or many
times vaster. Nay, even within the galactic zone
itself there are stars to which my theory gives as
noble proportions as the accepted views. For, in
the southern Coal-sack, there are minute telescopic
stars, as Sir John Herschel tells us, and these orbs,
according to the accepted views, must be regarded
as belonging to the galactic circle, though inexpli-
cably segregated from their fellows. According to
the views I have been led to form, many of these
telescopic stars must be regarded as suns lying far
beyond the galactic spiral, or perhaps associated with
outer whorls of this spiral which no telescope made
by man can ever reveal to us.

And this leads me to consider two phenomena
which are altogether inexplicable, I conceive, on any
theory except mine.

The first is the existence of excessively faint

streams of light—star-streams doubtless, though the components are not separately visible—in certain regions of the heavens. Sir John Herschel, who detected this strange phenomenon, speaks of the streams as so very faint that the idea of illusion has continually arisen subsequently; yet he dwells far too clearly on the characteristics of the phenomenon for any doubt to remain as to its reality. The faintest possible stippling of the field of view—the minute points of light being obviously *there*, though it was impossible to see them individually—a mottling which moved with the stars as he moved the tube to and fro, such are the terms in which Sir John Herschel speaks of this interesting phenomenon.

Now, no doubt whatever can exist that, if these faint streams really belong to the sidereal system, they are left altogether unaccounted for by the ordinary views respecting the structure of that system. There is no continuity between the stars composing them and even the minutest telescopic stars visible in the same general direction; so that a vast void must separate them from the outermost of those telescopic stars. According to my theory, they simply belong to outlying whorls of the spiral galaxy, and the telescopic stars seen upon them bear the same relation to them that the lucid stars bear to the Milky Way.

The second point is perhaps even more striking. In certain directions Sir John Herschel recognized the existence of two or more distinctly-marked classes of stars, as though, he says, definite sets of stars, separated by comparatively void intervals, lay in

those directions. It is clear that this association of
the stars into sets is as distinctly opposed to the
views ordinarily accepted as it is obviously an arrangement to be expected according to my theory
of the constitution of the sidereal system.

Quite early in my consideration of the subject I
am now upon, the idea suggested itself to me that
in the proper motions of the stars we have a means
of forming an estimate of the distances of these orbs;
and, further, of detecting any laws associating them
together, whether into streams or clusters; and that
the evidence thus obtained was likely to be in many
respects more trustworthy than that afforded by the
apparent magnitudes of the stars. Two processes of
inquiry suggested themselves. The first consisted in
a careful comparison of the mean motions of stars
of different apparent size, in order to determine
whether, on the average, small stars are so far off
that we can look upon them as in reality no smaller
on the average than those which appear larger. The
second consisted in charting down the proper motions, so as to detect any signs of star-drift which
might haply appear in different parts of the heavens.
I confess that I had not by any means expected
results so strikingly confirmatory of my views as
those I actually obtained.

The first method of inquiry, instead of giving an
average amount of proper motion to the smaller stars
somewhat, or perhaps even considerably, greater than
was to be expected, according to the theory which
sets these stars at an enormous distance, actually

gave them a mean motion *equal* to that of stars of the first three magnitudes. It became evident, then, that not only are small stars (I am here speaking of stars visible to the naked eye) mixed up as I had thought with bright stars visible in the same general direction, but that distance is less available to explain the smallness of the stars even than I had supposed. I had thought that certainly a large proportion of the small stars must in reality be very far from us; but it appeared that the proportion of stars whose smallness is so to be accounted for is in reality exceedingly minute. There must therefore be myriads of really small stars for every leading orb.

The second method of research led to the strange result that in many parts of the heavens a community of motion can be recognized, among star-groups far larger in extent than I had expected to find thus drifting through space. Knowing that, whatever view we form of the sidereal universe, we must yet recognize the fact that in every direction stars at very different distances must be visible, I had not hoped to find over any large region of space the traces of a community of motion. Nor even in small regions had I hoped to recognize very decided traces of star-drift, because I was conscious that, even with three or four stars really forming a drifting group, there would nearly always be found three or four others, either much further off or much nearer, and altogether dissociated from the drifting set. Indeed, I imagined, when I began the inquiry, that the most remarkable instance of star-drift in the heavens was that detected (though differently explained) by Baron Mädler in the constellation Taurus.

I found, however, that in other regions a far more obvious tendency to drift can be recognized. Perhaps the most remarkable instance of all is that illus-

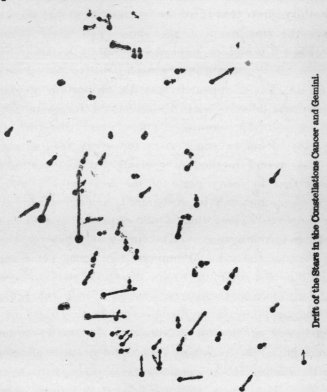

Drift of the Stars in the Constellations Cancer and Gemini.

trated in the accompanying plate. This picture represents the motions in the constellations Cancer and Gemini. It will be noticed that though here and there stars apparently not belonging to the system appear in the same range of view, yet the star-drift is unmistakable. The general parallelism of motion is very striking; and the difference in the amount of motion observed in different stars is only what was to be expected in a star-group whose range in distance, if equivalent to its lateral extent, must be such as fully to account for the range in the amount of apparent motion.

Fig. 6 exhibits one out of many parts of the

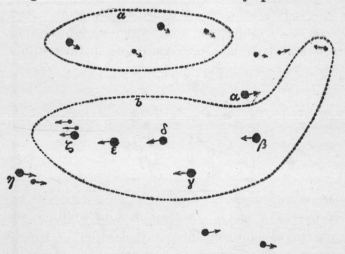

Fig. 6.—Observed Proper Motions of Stars in Ursa Major and Neighborhood.

heavens in which different sets of stars are observed to be drifting in different ways.

It will be seen that here there are three sets— those included in the space *a*, those in space *b*, and those left unenclosed, which are very obviously drifting, each in its special direction. The stars within the space *b* are *β*, *γ*, *δ*, *ε*, and *ζ*, of the Greater Bear, with three smaller stars. Their drift is, I think, most significant. If in truth the parallelism and equality of motion are to be regarded as accidental, the coincidence is one of a most remarkable character. But such an interpretation can hardly be looked upon as admissible, when we remember that the peculiarity is only one of a series of instances, some of which are scarcely less striking. One of these is presented in the accompanying figure in which the proper motions in the stars a, β, and γ, Arietis, and four other stars in the neighborhood, are exhibited.[1]

Here β and γ may be regarded as drifting with a,

Fig. 7.—Observed Proper Motions of Stars in Head of Aries.

but having a motion of their own in addition, sufficing to account for the want of strict parallelism between their apparent motion and that of a. The other stars seem obviously to belong to the same system.

I am led, by the facts which have here been briefly considered, rather to urge those who have time and inclination to inquire carefully into the minuter details of the sidereal heavens than to in-

---

[1] In all these figures the proper motion indicated by the length of the arrow attached to a star corresponds to the star's motion in thirty-six thousand years.

sist on any views of my own. While I recognize the wisdom and necessity of that course which the Herschels adopted in taking a wide view of the sidereal system, and in dealing rather with general results than with special peculiarities, I think the time has come when another course is possible and advisable. The Herschels having surveyed the field of heaven, it behooves us now to go over it with a close and searching scrutiny. To consider averages *now* is to level the scarcely perceptible undulations in our field of research, as well as its better-marked ridges or depressions; whereas we require, on the contrary, to exaggerate the variations of level, so that we may determine with more certainty what are the peculiarities presented by that most interesting field to man's contemplation. Or, to change the illustration, and to quote the words of the greatest living master of that kind of research which I have been advocating, "We must not be deterred from dwelling consecutively and closely on these speculative views by any idea of their hopelessness which the objectors against 'paper astronomy' may entertain, or by the real slenderness of the material threads out of which any connected theory of the universe has (at present) to be woven. '*Hypotheses fingo*' in this stage of our knowledge is quite as good a motto as Newton's '*Non fingo*'—provided always they be not hypotheses as to modes of physical action for which experience gives no warrant." [1]

---

[1] From a letter addressed by Sir J. Herschel to the present writer, August 1, 1869.

CHAPTER XII

IN the last chapter I have indicated reasons for believing that the sidereal system extends far beyond the range of the most powerful telescopes man has yet been able to construct. It need hardly be said that, supposing this view to be correct, we cannot possibly see any external galaxies, unless they surpass our own many thousands of times in richness and splendor. Every analogy that we have for our guidance points to the conclusion that, if our galaxy have limits, and there exist in space other galaxies, then those outer systems must be separated from ours by spaces exceeding the dimensions of the several galaxies many thousand or many million fold in extent. We know that the distances separating the satellites from their primaries exceed in an enormous ratio the dimensions of the satellites. The distances separating the planets from each other exceed in an enormous ratio the dimensions of the planets. The distances separating our solar system from others enormously exceed the dimensions of the various solar systems. And we may conclude that in all probability the distances separating our sidereal

(290)

system from other similar systems in space must exceed in an enormous ratio the dimensions of our galaxy, and of all other such systems.

That the sidereal system has limits I do not doubt. Of course it *may* be coextensive with space that is absolutely infinite in extent; but we have no reason for believing that, in rising step by step, from system to system, until we have reached the highest class of system known to us, we have reached the real summit of that perhaps altogether limitless range of steps. We know, indeed, that if light do not suffer extinction in traversing space (and we have as yet no evidence that it does), the extent of the sidereal system *must* be limited, since otherwise the whole of the starlit sky should shine with the brilliancy of sunlight.[1] And we may carry this argu-

---

[1] This is, perhaps, obvious; but, if not, the following proof may be accepted: Let the whole of space be conceived divided into spherical shells, having our earth at their centre, the thickness of each shell being τ. Then taking two shells, one at a distance r, the other at a distance r' (both r and r' much greater than τ), we see that the number of stars in these shells will be proportional to $r^2 \tau$ and $r'^2 \tau$ respectively; that is, will be independent of the thickness of the shell and vary as the square of its radius. (Here I am not concerned with those departures from uniformity which I have considered in the last chapter, because I suppose each shell large enough to include within it all varieties of distribution and aggregation. This applies, also, to what follows.) Now, the average apparent size of the stars of one shell will be to the average apparent size of stars in the other in the inverse proportion of the respective radii of the shells, the intrinsic brightness of the light received from the stars of each set being equal. Thus the total amount of light from the stars of one shell is to the total amount of light from stars in the other, as $r^2 \tau \times \dfrac{1}{r^2} : r'^2 \tau \times \dfrac{1}{r'^2}$ $1 : 1$.

Hence, supposing the amount of light received from one shell to be $\dfrac{1}{k}$th part of that which would be received if the whole celestial sphere were as

ment even further. For, though the sidereal system should be limited, but other systems similar to it spread throughout the infinity of space, there would still result this ineffable blaze of light, surpassing the light of day as greatly as the vault of heaven surpasses the disk of the sun. And this again would be true, though this system of systems were limited in extent, but surrounded by similar systems of systems in the infinity of space. And so on, let the order of systems which finally becomes infinite in number be what it may. There is only one way to escape from this limitless series of system-orders—that is, by accepting as true the hypothesis that light suffers extinction as it voyages through space. But it is worth noticing, when we are actually dealing with the infinity of space, and when, therefore, limitless conceptions are not paradoxical, but in reality as available for our purposes as finite conceptions would be, that if we do adopt the belief in an infinite succession of orders of systems, that is, first satellite-systems, then planetary-systems, then star-systems,

---

bright as the sun's, that is as a star's disk—k being inconceivably large, the amount received from the other is also $\frac{1}{k}$th of this amount, and the total from all the shells must, therefore, be $\frac{1}{k} + \frac{1}{k} + \frac{1}{k} + \frac{1}{k}$ —— to infinity.

Now, by taking k terms of this series (or k shells out of our infinite series of shells), we should get unity, that is, the whole heavens lighted up with starlight or sunlight. There would be a proportion of stars in the same visual line and so hiding each other; but, since we can take 2 k, 3 k, or *infinity* times k if need be, there can be no doubt the whole heavens would be lighted up with solar brightness.

then systems of star-systems, then systems of systems
of star-systems, and so on to infinity, and if we
accept as true of this infinite series what we know
to be true of the part within our ken, viz., that the
distance between the components forming any system
is indefinitely great compared with the dimensions of
those components, we no longer have as a conclusion
that the whole heavens should be lighted up with
stellar (that is with solar) splendor; even though, in
this view of the subject, there are in reality an infinite number of stars, just as in the view according
to which the sidereal system extends without inter-
ruption to infinity.[1]

---

[1] It is clear that we no longer get, as in the previous note, a series of
equal small terms. If we take our infinite series of shells as before, we get
for the sidereal system n times $\frac{1}{k}$ where n is finite and therefore $\frac{n}{k}$ finite.

We must indeed assume $\frac{n}{k}$ to be small, and so of other similar ratios presently to be dealt with. With respect to the system of systems we have
these considerations to guide us—any of the spherical shells within this
system must supply to our skies an amount of light indefinitely less than
one of the shells within the sidereal system itself, say $\frac{1}{k'}$th part only, k' indefinitely large; but the number of shells falling within that system is very
much greater, say n' times as great where n' is finite. Therefore we get for
the total amount of light coming from the system of systems a quantity
proportional to $\frac{nn'}{kk'}$, and so for the system of system of systems we get a
quantity proportional to $\frac{nn'}{kk'}\frac{n''}{k''}$, where k'' is indefinitely large, n'' very
large. And for each successive order we get a multiplier of the form $\frac{N}{K}$,
where K is indefinitely large and N very large indeed. Suppose $\frac{v}{K}$ to be the

But whether we adopt this or any other view of
the way in which external systems are arranged, this

---

largest of all these multipliers, then the total amount of light received
from the infinite system of systems is proportional to less than

$$\frac{n}{k}\left(1+\frac{\nu}{\kappa}+\frac{\nu^2}{\kappa^2}+\frac{\nu^3}{\kappa^3} \ldots \text{ to infinity}\right),$$

(in which ν is supposed to be less than κ, *i.e.*, to less than $\dfrac{n}{k}\left(\dfrac{\kappa}{\kappa-\nu}\right)$, a

finite quantity, which will even be minute if k and κ are severally much
greater than n and ν.

This particular mode of escaping from the difficulty suggested by the
illumination of the heavens, without adopting the theory that light suffers
extinction in its passage through space, occurred to me while I was preparing a series of papers entitled "A New Theory of the Universe," which
appeared in "The Student" in the spring of 1869, and I there exhibit the
considerations just dealt with. I was much pleased to find, from a letter
of Sir John Herschel's, that the same idea had suggested itself to him; as
I was thus encouraged to believe that I had not gone very far astray in the
whole series of papers, whereof the matter in question had seemed to me
the most speculative portion. The following are the words in which Sir
John Herschel, writing in ignorance of my having adopted the same view,
expresses the ideas above dealt with: "One of the arguments advanced in
favor of the spatial extinction of light was that, if there is not such extinction, the whole heavens ought to be one blaze of solar light—admitting
the universe to be infinite, because it was contended that there could then
be no direction in space in which the visual ray would not encounter a star
(*i.e.*, a sun). This argument is fallacious, for it is easy to imagine a constitution of a universe literally infinite which would allow of any amount
of such directions of penetration as *not* to encounter a star. Granting that
it consists of systems subdivided according to the law that every higher
order of bodies in it should be immensely more distant from the centre than
those of the next inferior order—this would happen. Thus, in our own,
the moon is very near the earth, the satellites to their primaries. These
primaries are immensely more distant from the sun, *their* centre; the fixed
stars again still *more* immensely more remote from the sun. Suppose *our*
system to terminate with the visible fixed stars; then imagine a system of
such systems as remote from each other, *in comparison with their own
dimensions*, as the distance of the fixed stars in comparison with the planetary system; such systems seen from each other would subtend no greater
angle than a star seen from the sun—and so on."

at any rate is certain, that if the stars at the outer parts of our own sidereal system be beyond the ken of our most powerful instruments—and I have shown that there are strong reasons for this conclusion—then the component suns of external galaxies cannot by any possibility be visible. So that, according to this view, all resolvable nebulæ, at least, must be dismissed from the category of external galaxies. Nor will it be thought probable that irresolvable nebulæ are external galaxies, if once that view of the extent of the sidereal system is adopted.

But there are independent considerations, on which I prefer now to dwell, for believing that all the nebulæ belong to the sidereal system.

It will hardly be necessary, let me remark in passing, for me to point out how this matter is associated with the subject of other worlds. It is true that, when once it is admitted that there are external galaxies, it may be looked on as a matter of small importance (so far as the subject of this treatise is concerned) whether we can actually see those galaxies or not. I am not, for instance, in the same position as Dr. Whewell, who assigned to the nebulæ what I take to be their true place in the universe, with the express object of overthrowing the belief that there exist other galaxies as vast as the sidereal or vaster, thronged with suns which are severally the centres of planetary systems, within which again are worlds as well suited to be the abode of life as this earth on which we dwell. But, though my purpose is different from his, it is equally

necessary that I should insist on the true position of
the nebulæ. Because, if these objects form indeed
part of the sidereal system, the relations they present
are of extreme importance. They exhibit to us
within the bounds of our galaxy systems altogether
different from the solar system, and thus suggest
ideas of other classes of worlds peopled with their
own peculiar forms of life, as distinct, perchance,
even in their general characteristics, from any found
amid the systems circling round stars, as the forms
of life in Venus or in Mars must be in their special
characteristics from those existing on our own earth.

Freed from those analogies which led the elder
Herschel to regard the stellar nebulæ—resolvable and
irresolvable¹—as external star-systems, let us consider
the relations presented by these and other nebulæ,
without reference to preconceived opinions.

We must first pay attention to one of the most
striking of the discoveries which the spectroscope has
yet enabled man to make—the discovery that certain
nebulæ are gaseous. It is necessary to consider this
significant discovery, rather than those which were
the first to exhibit the real place of the nebulæ in
our scheme, because we shall thus be able to divide
the nebulæ at once into two great classes, instead of
being led to this arrangement by following out the
history of those long processes of research by which

¹ By irresolvable stellar nebulæ, I mean those nebulæ which, though
not resolvable into stars, yet present the characteristic features which lead
astronomers to believe that only increase of telescopic power is needed in
order to effect resolution.

the two great orders of nebulæ were long since separated from each other under the piercing scrutiny
of Sir William Herschel.

The reader will see how the spectroscope could at
once resolve a question which ordinary observations
would be all but powerless to deal with. The nebulæ being self-luminous, the nature of the matter
which is the source of their light would be shown
by the character of the spectrum, as distinctly as
though that matter were actually present in the
laboratory of the spectroscopist.

Mr. Huggins thus describes the observation which
first revealed the true nature of certain orders of the
nebulæ. The object under examination was a nebula in Draco, belonging to the class of planetary
nebulæ: "On August 19, 1864, I directed the telescope, armed with the spectrum apparatus, to this
nebula. At first I suspected some derangement of
the instrument had taken place, for no spectrum was
seen, but only a short line of light perpendicular to
the direction of dispersion (that is, to what would in
the case of solar light be the *length* of the spectrum).
I then found that the light of this nebula, unlike any
other ex-terrestrial light which had yet been subjected by me to prismatic analysis, was not composed
of light of different refrangibilities, and therefore
could not form a spectrum. A great part of the
light from this nebula is monochromatic, and after
passing through the prisms remains concentrated in
a bright line, occupying the position of that part of
the spectrum to which its light corresponds in re-

frangibility. A more careful examination, however, showed that—a little more refrangible than the bright line, and separated from it by a dark interval—a narrower and much fainter line occurs. Beyond this again, at about three times the distance of the second line, a third exceedingly faint line was seen. The positions of these lines in the spectrum were determined by a simultaneous comparison of them in the instrument, with the spectrum of the induction-spark taken between electrodes of magnesium. The strongest line coincides in position with the brightest of the air-lines. This line is due to nitrogen. . . . The faintest of the lines of the nebula agrees in position with a line of hydrogen. The other bright line was not found to correspond with a known line of any terrestrial element. Besides the bright lines, an exceedingly faint spectrum was just perceived for a short distance on both sides of the group of bright lines." Mr. Huggins suspected that this was not uniform, but crossed with dark spaces. Subsequent observations on other nebulæ[1] induced him "to regard

---

[1] One of the most interesting of Mr. Huggins' researches into the subject of the light of nebulæ is his attempt to determine its intrinsic brilliancy. By comparing the light of certain gaseous nebulæ with that of a sperm-candle (of the size called six to the pound), he found that these objects, assumed to be continuous, shine with a light varying in intrinsic brilliancy from the 1,500th to the 20,000th of that of such a candle. By a strange misconception, Mr. Lockyer, in discussing Mr. Huggins' result, speaks of the comparison as though it related to the absolute brightness of the nebulæ, saying that "such a candle a quarter of a mile off is 20,000 times more brilliant than the nebula." Mr. Huggins' result is wholly distinct from this, and much more important. His comparison relates to the intrinsic luminosity of the nebular substance, not to the *quantity* of

this faint spectrum as due to the solid or liquid matter of the nucleus, and as quite distinct from the bright lines into which nearly the whole of the light from the nebula is concentrated.''

Thus was solved a problem which had, for the best part of a century, perplexed astronomers. There was not, indeed, a full answer to all the questions of interest associated with the problem. But it had been laid down by Sir William Herschel, as a legitimate conclusion from observation, that certain orders of the nebulæ are gaseous, and astronomers had ranged themselves for and against this proposition. Telescopic improvements had seemed at length to turn the scale in favor of those who held Sir William Herschel to have been mistaken. Already the problem had seemed all but definitively settled: and then in a moment this observation by Mr. Huggins had reversed the whole matter. It was now established, beyond all possibility of future question, that, on the main point, the greatest of modern astronomers had been altogether in the right.

The orders of nebulæ which give a spectrum of bright lines would seem from Mr. Huggins' observations to be (1) the planetary nebulæ, (2) the ring nebulæ, (3) the irregular nebulæ. The spiral nebulæ seem, for the most part, to give a continuous spectrum, but some of these objects give the bright-line spectrum indicative of gaseity. The orders of nebulæ

---

light received from the nebulæ. (The distance of the candle in Mr. Huggins' observations is not considered in the result; it was a mere matter of convenience.)

which give a continuous spectrum appear to be the following: (1) star groups, (2) clusters, regular and irregular, and (3) easily resolvable nebulæ. Of the irresolvable nebulæ a large proportion seem to be gaseous.[1]

Here, then, we find the nebulæ ranged into two important divisions, apparently separated by a distinct line of demarcation. Yet one is tempted to inquire whether these divisions may not in reality run into each other, by the fact that among nebulæ of certain orders are objects belonging to both divisions. And the fact that, beneath the bright-line spectrum of the gaseous nebulæ, a faint continuous spectrum may be seen, seems also to point in the same direction. We know that, so far as the telescopic appearance of the nebulæ is concerned, there is very striking evidence of a gradual progression from clusters to irresolvable nebulæ, and, therefore,

---

[1] The following classification of nebulæ in this respect, by Lord Oxmantown, is interesting as indicating the results of observations made with so powerful an instrument as the great Parsonstown telescope (the six-foot reflector):

	Continuous Spectrum.	Gaseous Spectrum.
Clusters	10	0
Certainly or probably resolved ? . . .	5	0
Certainly or probably resolvable ? . . .	10	6
Blue, or green, no resolvability	0	4
No resolvability detected	6	5
Total observed	31	15

Adding nebulæ not observed at Parsonstown, there are in all 41 which exhibited a continuous spectrum, and 19 which gave a spectrum indicative of gaseity.

we are led to inquire, whether the spectroscope conveys a similar lesson.

Now, this question could only be answered satisfactorily by the observation of a series of nebulæ having spectra progressively varying, from bright lines on an almost invisible continuous spectrum to a continuous spectrum with the same bright lines superposed on it, but almost imperceptible, because their brightness so little exceeded that of the continuous spectrum. We have not evidence of such completeness. But Lieutenant Herschel has observed in the southern heavens a clustering nebula with a continuous spectrum, on which he could just detect the three bright lines seen in the spectra of the gaseous nebulæ. And, so far as this evidence extends, the conclusion is obvious, that the various orders of nebulæ are orders of but a single family. It will be seen presently that this conclusion, which is strikingly corroborated by other evidence, has a very important bearing on the views we are to form respecting the relations between the nebulæ and the sidereal system.

The first process by which we must attempt to form a correct estimate of the nebular system corresponds to Sir William Herschel's process of star-gauging. We must inquire according to what general laws the nebulæ are spread over the vault of heaven.

Now, when this is done, it appears that there is a well-marked peculiarity in the arrangement of the nebulæ, a peculiarity as striking as the existence of the galactic circle itself. *The nebulæ seem to with-*

draw themselves from the neighborhood of the galaxy.
In the northern heavens they cluster very definitely
toward the pole of the galaxy; in the southern they
are arranged in streams and clustering aggregations,
but the galaxy itself is, in either case, left almost
clear of nebulæ.

If this peculiarity is accidental, the coincidence
involved is most remarkable. Had there been a zone
of nebulæ, and that zone had shown a tendency to
coincidence with the Milky Way, the relation would
have been held strikingly indicative of a real association between the nebular and the sidereal systems.
But is the direct converse of this relation more
likely to be the effect of chance? Have not observers and experimenters concluded (in every other similar instance) that a law of contrast is as indicative
of a real connection as a law of association? It is
surprising, therefore, that nearly all astronomers, who
have considered the relation in question, have regarded it as affording strong evidence that the nebular system is wholly dissociated from the sidereal.

Next let us turn to special features. In the first
place, let us inquire whether the different orders of
nebulæ exhibit any peculiarities of arrangement.

We find that clusters exhibit a very marked preference for the neighborhood of the Milky Way; resolvable nebulæ seem to prefer the galactic zone, but
not in so decided a manner; and it is only among
the irresolvable nebulæ that we recognize that withdrawal from the Milky Way which had seemed characteristic of the whole nebular system, before we

considered its several orders. The fact that the
irresolvable nebulæ form about four-fifths of the
total number will account for the circumstance that
a peculiarity really appertaining to that order alone
should appear to belong to the whole system of
nebulæ.

Again, the planetary and irregular nebulæ are
found to affect the neighborhood of the Milky Way.
I have already mentioned that these objects are
gaseous.

It is easy to see what general conclusions may be
deduced from the peculiarities here touched upon.
Obviously the first shows us most distinctly that
there is a relation between propinquity to the Milky
Way and the character of nebulæ as respects resolvability—a relation which points in the most decisive
manner to the existence of a close association between the sidereal system, of which the Milky Way
certainly forms part, and the nebular system, from
which clusters and resolvable nebulæ cannot reasonably be separated. It is equally obvious that the
second peculiarity indicates the existence of a close
association between the Milky Way and the character of the nebulæ as respects gaseity; a relation
which brings all the gaseous nebulæ into close association with the sidereal system, since we know that
among the extra-galactic nebulæ there are many
which are principally formed of the very same
gases which appear in the irregular and planetary
nebulæ. When we consider that those peculiarities
of configuration and of constitution which have alike

seemed to indicate that the various orders of nebulæ
merge into each other by indefinable gradations are
both associated, in a very distinct manner, with the
most marked peculiarity of the sidereal system, and
when to this we add what has been already suggested by the relation of contrast between the irresolvable nebulæ and the Milky Way, the conclusion
seems forcibly impressed upon us that the nebular
and the sidereal systems are but different parts of
one single scheme.

But I pass on to other evidence, independent of
what has hitherto been adduced, and pointing with
equal force to the same conclusion.

In the northern heavens it is not very easy to
exhibit any general law of arrangement associating
the nebulæ and the fixed stars. For reasons which
yet remain to be detected, there are in fact many
marked points of difference between the whole character of the heavens on the northern and on the
southern side of the galactic zone. But even in the
northern heavens one peculiarity has been remarked,
which is well worthy of careful consideration. Sir
William Herschel, while prosecuting his series of
researches among stars and nebulæ, was struck by
the circumstance that, after sweeping over a part
of the heavens which was unusually barren, he
commonly met with nebulæ; insomuch that it was
his practice at such times to call to his assistant (his
sister, Miss Caroline Herschel) to "prepare for nebulæ." This peculiarity was noticed also by Sir John
Herschel.

Now, what are we to understand by such a relation as this? Can we suppose that, owing to some strange accident, external galaxies have been placed always opposite the barest regions of the sidereal system? Or, setting aside such a notion as obviously incredible, are we to imagine that, when searching over those barren regions, the astronomer has a better chance of detecting nebulæ than where stars are more richly strewn, because the sky is less filled with glare? We are forced to dismiss this notion, that the barren regions of the heavens are thus in a manner the spy-holes of the sidereal system, by the fact (presently, and for another purpose, to be dwelt on more at length) that in the Magellanic Clouds, where stars of all magnitudes are richly strewn, nebulæ, even down to the very faintest orders, are more abundant than in any other region of the heavens. We have, then, no other conclusion to form, but that the association thus observed between starless regions and richness of nebular distribution indicates a very close relation indeed between stars and nebulæ; that, in fact, *the nebulæ in a sense represent the missing stars; that the region where those nebulæ appear has been drained of star-material, so to speak, in order to form them.*

In the southern heavens yet clearer proof exists of an association between the stellar and nebular systems. We do not recognize in the northern skies any well-marked star-streams. In the southern skies, however, such streams have been recognized from the earliest ages. The constellations Hydra and

Eridanus, the two streams from the Water-can of
Aquarius, and the band between the two fishes,[1]
indicate how clearly the ancients traced certain well-
marked star-streams. The moderns have traced the
extension of some of these streams in the constellations Grus, Hydra, Reticulum, etc., into the near
neighborhood of the southern pole. Now, the nebulæ in the southern heavens exhibit a well-marked
tendency to aggregate into streams. So that, in this
mere resemblance between the general characteristics
of the stellar and nebular systems in the southern
heavens, we have a somewhat remarkable evidence
of association. But when we consider the disposition
of the two sets of streams—the stellar and the nebular—this evidence is very much strengthened. There
is found to be a well-marked correspondence between
the nebular and stellar streams, not merely as respects general position, but even in minute details—
the nebular streams following the windings of the
stellar ones. Such a relation would be very remarkable, even were it observed but in a single instance.
Since, however, all the well-marked star-streams in
the southern heavens are associated with well-marked
nebular streams, no doubt can remain that the relation is not a mere coincidence, but indicates a real
association between the nebular and stellar systems.

But yet more striking evidence remains to be
considered.

In the southern heavens there are two strange

---

[1] Though Pisces is not a southern constellation, yet it is south of the
galactic circle, to which I am for the moment referring the constellations.

clouds of milky light, which have long been known by sailors as the Magellanic Clouds, but are commonly called by astronomers the Nubeculæ. Each of these objects, when examined with the telescope, is found to be constituted, like the Milky Way, of multitudes of small stars. But, unlike the Milky Way, the Nubeculæ contain within their bounds many nebulæ of all orders. In fact, each of the Nubeculæ is at once a star-cluster and a cluster of nebulæ.

Now, there can be no doubt whatever that the association here is not accidental, that we do not by some strange chance see a great star-cluster in the same direction as a much more distant and much vaster cluster of external galaxies. Nor, again, can there be any doubt that the generally circular figure of each Nubecula indicates a general approach to the spherical form in the case of each cluster. The probability that by some strange accident a cluster of cylindrical shape[1] might be so placed as to exhibit to us a circular figure is exceedingly small; but the chance that two such clusters should be presented in so exceptional a manner may be regarded as evanescent. We are compelled, then, to believe that, within the limits of spheres so placed as to subtend a small angle to the eye, stars of all magnitudes between the seventh and the twelfth inclusive are mixed up with nebulæ of all degrees of resolvability. "Taking the apparent semi-diameter of the Nubecula Major at

---

[1] Or, more correctly, a cluster shaped like a long frustrum of a gigantic cone.

three degrees," says Sir John Herschel, "and regarding its solid form as, roughly speaking, spherical, its nearest and most remote parts differ in their
distance from us by a little more than a tenth part
of our distance from its centre." "It must therefore
be taken as a demonstrated fact," he adds presently,
"that stars of the seventh and eighth magnitude and
irresolvable nebulæ may coexist within limits of distance not differing in proportion more than as nine
to ten." This demonstrated fact of Sir John Herschel's is the very fact to which I had been led by
other considerations, the fact, namely, that the nebulæ are not external galaxies, but intimately associated with the sidereal system of which in fact they
form part and parcel. Dr. Whewell, accepting Sir
John Herschel's reasoning as conclusive on the
point, adopted the same view. Yet Sir John Herschel himself seems, immediately after establishing
this noteworthy conclusion, to have been prepared
to abandon it, at least as a demonstrated fact, since
he says of it only that "it must inspire some degree
of caution in admitting *as certain*" facts directly opposed to it. It must not be forgotten, however, that
to the clear vision of this great astronomer the association between nebulæ and fixed stars *had* presented
itself as a demonstrated fact; that, even in the latest
editions of his noble work on astronomy, he has not
altered the words in which he has spoken of that
association; and that so able a reasoner as Dr. Whewell has chosen rather to accept what Herschel has
spoken of as a demonstrated fact, than to adopt that

measure of caution which Herschel subsequently advocated.

Lastly, and perhaps most strikingly of all, the association between stars and nebulæ is indicated by the obvious connection between the figure of the irregular nebulæ and the arrangement of the star-groups seen in the same field of view. There is not one of the irregular nebulæ which does not exhibit this peculiarity in the most striking manner. This may be asserted even of those nebulæ with respect to which Sir John Herschel has remarked that the arrangement may be, and probably is, purely accidental. His own pictures prove in the most convincing manner that no such explanation can be accepted. Were the peculiarity confined to the feature Herschel limits his attention to, one might adopt his explanation. The mere aggregation of a large number of stars on the very heart of a nebula might be an accident. The fact, for instance, that the great irregular nebula surrounding the star Eta Argûs agrees exactly in position with the greatest condensation of the wonderfully rich portion of the Milky Way on which that surprising variable lies, might be a mere coincidence, though in any case it would be a strange one. But when one examines the structure of this and similar nebulæ, and finds that the stars are arranged in a manner most obviously related to the arrangement of the nebular condensations (or folds as one may almost say), one cannot doubt that a real and intimate bond of association exists between the stars and the neb-

ulous masses around them. If the extension of
the milky light of the great Orion nebula to the
star in the sword, which is centrally involved in
strong nebulosity, to ε in the belt, which is similarly
involved, and to several other stars in the constellation all alike in being regions of increased nebular
condensation, be a mere accidental coincidence, then
the laws of probability had better be forgotten as
soon as possible, for, as at present understood, they
can only serve to lead men astray.

It will be noticed, as respects the two proofs on
which I have last dwelt, that they seem directly
opposed to those which I first quoted. One cannot argue, it might be urged, that the nebulæ are
associated with the sidereal system because they are
least numerous where there are most stars, and *vice
versa;* while at the same time one draws the same
conclusion from the aggregation of the nebulæ in
streams or clusters where there are streams and
clusters of stars, or from the fact that stars are
seen actually mixed up with nebulous matter. At
first sight this objection seems just; but, on consideration, it will be found that, in reality, the two
seemingly contrary lines of argument bear in the
same direction. When we find the nebulæ gathered
where stars are wanting, and *vice versa*, we conclude
that there is some reason for this peculiarity, and
that that reason must involve some sort of association between the nebulæ and the stars; we see,
further, that the relation is accounted for if we
suppose that, in these cases, either the formation

of nebulæ has drained a region of material from which single stars would otherwise have been formed, or *vice versa*. Why, in a particular region, the formation of nebulæ should be encouraged, while the formation of stars should be checked, we cannot say; nor can we account for the contrary peculiarity in another region; but we feel certain that some cause must exist for both relations, because the results are too marked to be the result of accident. Now, in the case where we find both stars and nebulæ abundant in particular parts of the heavens, we feel equally certain that the result is not accidental. Even though there were not here, as in the former case, the evidence of a clearing of star-material from certain regions, we could not doubt that the association of stars and nebulæ was real and not apparent. But in reality there is *here*, precisely as in the former case, a gathering together of stellar matter into certain regions. The very existence of such a stream as Eridanus or Hydra, and of such a cluster as the greater or lesser Magellanic Cloud, implies the action of such a process of segregation. A stream would not be recognizable if it were not bounded by relatively bare regions. Clusters like the Nubeculæ *might* be visible even on a rich sky, and were the sidereal heavens richly strewed with stars round these objects I should be disposed to admit that there was a difficulty in my theory. But what is the fact? Not only is each of the Nubeculæ placed in a region obviously bare of lucid stars, but Sir John Herschel, speaking of the telescopic aspect of the neighborhood of these mysterious clusters, dwells again and again on its poverty. "A miserably poor and barren region," he says of one field near the Nubeculæ. "The access to the Nubeculæ," he says elsewhere, "is on all sides through a *desert.*" What evidence could more clearly point to the fact that these great clusters are gathered out from a vast region of space? Their internal structure teaches us how such a process of segregation leads to the birth of nebulæ, as well as stars. The whole history of the sidereal system is indeed taught us in the Magellanic Clouds and the great streams of intermixed stars and nebulæ which flow toward them as rivers toward some mighty lake. We see the wonder-working forces of gravitation extending their influences throughout vast regions of space, gathering in the materials spread throughout that space, here forming stars, there nebulæ, changing the element of distance into various forms of force—heat and light, electricity and magnetism — and finally (though in what special way we are as yet unable to perceive) making the orbs which it has formed the seats of life, or subservient, more or less directly, to the wants of living creatures.

CHAPTER XIII

SUPERVISION AND CONTROL

IT has been customary, in treatises on the plurality
of worlds, to discuss the religious difficulties
which seem to suggest themselves when man
regards the universe around him as thronged with
worlds, each peopled with millions of living creatures, and many perchance the abode of intelligent
and therefore responsible beings. Accustomed to regard himself as in a special manner the object of
God's care and solicitude, it is not without a sense
of pain that he is brought to contemplate the possibility that other creatures may exist in uncounted
millions whom God regards with infinite love and interest. "If this be so," asks Whewell, "how shall
the earth and men, its inhabitants, *annihilated* as it
were by the magnitude of the known universe, continue to be anything in the regard of Him who em-
braces all? Least of all, how shall men continue to
receive that special, preserving, providential, judicial,
personal care, which religion implies; and without
the belief in which, any man who has religious
thoughts must be disturbed and unhappy, desolate
and forsaken?"

I do not, however, feel by any means invited to
consider "the religious difficulty" by the success
which has attended the efforts made by others to
remove it. I find that, while, on the one hand,
the thoughtful and conscientious men who have in
a special manner considered the difficulty have been
(in relation at least to revealed religion) at issue
among each other, their views have not, on the
other hand, been found acceptable even by a few
among their readers. I doubt almost, when I judge
from the comments which have been made on this
part of the works of Chalmers, Whewell, Brewster,
and others, whether a single reader of those works
has found the religious views of any one of their
authors congenial with his own.

It is specially noteworthy that even where, as in
the case of Brewster and Chalmers, two writers adopt
the same view of the general question of other
worlds, they yet hold altogether different views
as to the bearing of that question upon the subject of religion.

It is very doubtful, therefore, whether it is a
wise thing, whether it is conducive to the purpose
of any one thus conscientiously discussing the religious aspect of our question, to present his own
personal views on the subject of revealed religion.
If I thought otherwise, I should not shrink from
the task of indicating the sufficiently definite views
which I entertain myself upon this subject. But I
apprehend that, apart from the consideration that the
reader must be wholly indifferent about them, my

indicating them would have an effect the very reverse of that which I should desire.[1]

Merely remarking, therefore, that in considering the infinity of God's beneficence we must remember this quality of infinity, that it comprises many infinities, I pass on to considerations which seem to fall more naturally within the province of the student of science.

It is a peculiarity of the subject of other worlds than ours, that it suggests, more strikingly than any other, certain difficulties in connection with the conceptions we are to form as to the supervision and control exercised by the Creator over His works. We feel that if we are to believe, as we must believe, in an infinitely powerful and wise God, we must not merely regard all the worlds which people space as objects of His regard, but every event, however seemingly insignificant, occurring in any, even the least important of His worlds, as an essential part of the plan according to which all things were created from the beginning.

But here already—such is the nature of the sub-

---

[1] Where Bacon has selected to be silent, few can without presumption venture to lay down their opinions as of weight in matters connected with revealed religion. The argument which follows may not indeed be acceptable to many, but few will doubt the wisdom of the conclusion to which he comes. "If we were disposed," he says, "to survey the realm of sacred or inspired theology, we must quit the small vessel of human reason, and put ourselves on board the ship of the Church, which alone possesses the Divine needle for justly shaping the course. Nor will the stars of philosophy, that have hitherto principally lent their light, be of further service to us; and *therefore it were not improper to be silent upon the subject*."—*Advancement of Learning*, Book IX.

ject I am to deal with—I have been forced to use terms which have really no proper application to the Almighty and His works. I have spoken of the creation of all things, whereas, in the sense in which men can alone interpret such words, we cannot reasonably conceive that there ever was a creation; and I have spoken of the beginning, whereas we cannot conceive that there ever was a beginning in the sense implied.[1]

Let us consider definitely (even though we must be unable to conceive clearly or at all) the infinities we have to deal with.

We know that space must be infinite. If the region amid which stars and nebulæ are scattered with so great profusion be limited, if beyond lies on all sides a vast void, or if, instead, there be material bounds enclosing the universe of worlds on every hand, yet where are the limits of void or bound? Infinity of space, occupied or unoccupied, there must undoubtedly be. Of this infinity it has been finely said, that its centre is everywhere, its boundary nowhere. Now, whether within this infinity of space there be an infinity of matter, is a question which we cannot so certainly answer. Only, if we were to accept *this* as certain, that the proportion which unoccupied bears to occupied space cannot be infinitely great—a view which at least seems reasonable and probable—then it would follow that matter as well

---

[1] To prevent any possibility of my meaning being misinterpreted here, I point out that I have been obliged myself to use the terms of which I speak as inexact.

as space must be infinite, since any finite proportion of infinity must itself also be infinite. So that, regarding occupied space as the realm over which the Almighty's control is exercised, and over which His supervision extends, we find just reason for looking upon that realm as no less infinite than the infinity of space in which it is contained.

Time also must undoubtedly be infinite. If the portion of time which has hitherto been, or which will hereafter be, occupied with the occurrence of events (of whatever sort) were preceded and will be followed by a vast void interval, yet there can be neither beginning nor end to either of those bounding voids. Infinity of time, occupied or unoccupied, there must undoubtedly be. And, though it is not possible for us to know certainly that there has been no beginning, or that there will be no end to that portion of time which is occupied with the occurrence of *events* (of whatever sort), yet it appears so unreasonable to conceive that unoccupied time bears an infinitely great proportion to occupied time, that we seem forced to the conclusion that occupied time is infinite—or, more definitely, that there has been no beginning and will be no end to the sequence of events throughout the infinitely-extended realm of the Almighty.

And thus we are forced to believe in the infinite wisdom and the infinite power of God; since to conceive of limits to the wisdom and power of Him whose realm is infinite in extent and in duration is obviously to conclude that the Ruler is infinitely

incompetent to rule over His kingdom; for there can
be no relation between the finite and the infinite save
the relation of infinite disproportion.

Now, although the conception of God as a spirit—
omnipresent, eternal, omnipotent, and omniscient—is
altogether beyond the powers of man's imagination,
yet we may consider certain relations between the
way in which He views the universe and the modes
in which we men consider the various matters falling either under our supervision and partial control,
or of which we can in any way or to any extent
become cognizant.

Senses such as we have we can no more attribute
to God than we can assign to Him hands and feet.
Nor can we conceive in what way a spirit, as He is,
is cognizant of material processes which we only
recognize through their material effects. Yet, as
we do not doubt that God is cognizant of the actual
state of the universe at any moment we cannot doubt
that He is cognizant of all those processes by which
our senses can be affected. And clearly, He not
only recognizes all these processes in such sort that
he may be said to see what we see, to hear what we
hear, and so on; but effects which, though related
to vision, hearing, or the like, are infinitely too minute to be appreciated by our senses, must be as
obvious to God as the light of day or the roar of
thunder to ourselves.

But, before considering the nature of God's supervision of His universe, we may proceed a step
further. The senses we possess are sufficient to

indicate to us the possible existence of senses not merely far more acute, but of a wholly different kind. By the sense of touch, for instance, we can indeed recognize the feeling of heat; but it is easy to conceive of a sense (analogous to that by which light is made to teach us of the aspect of external objects) enabling men to judge of the figure, substance, internal structure, and other qualities of an object, by the action of the heat-waves proceeding from it. Or again electricity might, instead either of light or of heat, be the means of communicating intelligence as to the qualities of objects. We can conceive also of a sense bearing the same analogy to sight that the spectroscope bears to the telescope. And a hundred kinds of sense, or, in other words, a hundred modes of receiving intelligence about what exists or is going on around us, might be readily conceived. Now, we cannot doubt that the natural processes involved in every such mode of conveying impressions to material creatures must be infinitely more obvious to God than we can possibly conceive them to be to material beings.

Yet once more, we know that reason is able to range beyond the action of the senses. Man is able to assure himself that events have happened which yet have produced no direct effect upon any of his senses. By the exercise of reason he becomes as well assured of such events as though they had actually passed before his eyes. We must assume that an analogous power, but infinite in degree, infinitely rapid in its operation, and infinite in the extent of space and time over which it ranges, is possessed by the Almighty.

And now let us notice some of the conclusions to which these considerations tend.

Let us first deal with the teachings of that sense which is the most far-reaching[1] of all the faculties given to man—the sense of sight.

In a little treatise called "The Stars and the Earth," published anonymously several years since, some results of modern discoveries respecting light were dealt with in a very interesting manner. I propose to follow the path of thought indicated in that treatise, as a fitting introduction to wider conceptions of the supervision and control exercised by the Almighty over His universe.

We know from Römer's researches, and even more surely from the phenomenon termed the aberration of the fixed stars, that light does not travel with infinite velocity. Its speed is indeed so enormous, that, compared with every form of motion with which we are familiar, the velocity of light appears infinitely great. In a single second light traverses a space equal to eight times the circumference of the earth; and therefore, in travelling from any visible object on the earth to the eye of a terrestrial ob-

---

[1] Most persons, if asked which sense comes next to sight in this respect, would answer hearing. Yet *touch*—or rather *feeling*—has a range far exceeding that of hearing, since we can feel the heat emitted by the sun. Nor is it difficult to conceive of such an increase in the delicacy of the sense of touch, that even the minute amount of heat received from the fixed stars might be felt, and so the range of the sense extended many million-fold.

server, light occupies a space of time indefinitely short. Yet, even as regards such objects as these, light has occupied a real interval of time, however minute, in reaching the eye; insomuch that we see objects not as they are at the moment we perceive them, but as they were the minutest fraction of a second before.

Raising our eyes from the earth to regard the celestial objects, we find, in place of the indefinitely minute interval before considered, a really appreciable space of time occupied by light in carrying to us information as to the condition of those distant orbs. From the moon, light takes little more than a second and a quarter in reaching us, so that we obtain sufficiently early information of the condition of our satellite. But light occupies more than eight minutes in reaching us from the sun, a longer or shorter interval in travelling to us from Mercury, Venus, and Mars, according to the position of these planets, from about thirty-five to about fifty minutes in reaching us from Jupiter, about an hour and twenty minutes on the average in speeding across the great gap which separates us from Saturn, while we receive intelligence from Uranus and Neptune only after intervals respectively twice and three times as great as that which light takes in reaching us from the ringed planet.

Thus, if we could at any instant view the whole range of the solar system as distinctly as we see Jupiter or Mars when in opposition, the scene presented to us would not indicate the real aspect of the solar system at that, or indeed at any definite instant. Precisely as a daily newspaper gives us a later account of what is going on in London than of events happening in the provinces, of these than of events on the Continent, and of these again than of occurrences taking place in America, Asia, Africa, or Australasia, so the intelligence brought by light respecting the various members of, the solar system belongs to different epochs. And if man had powers of vision enabling him to watch what is taking place on the different planets of the solar system, it is clear that events of the utmost importance might have transpired—under his very eyes, so to speak—while yet he remained wholly unconscious of their recurrence. Or, to invert the illustration, if an observer on Neptune could see all that is taking place on the earth, he might remain for hours quite unconscious of an event important enough to affect the welfare of a whole continent, though that event should happen under his eyes, and his visual powers be such as I have supposed. We can imagine, for example, an observer on Neptune watching the battle of Waterloo from the early dawn until the hour when Napoleon's heart was yet full of hope, and our great captain was watching with ever-growing anxiety, as charge after charge threatened to destroy the squares on whose steadfastness depended the fate of a continent. We can conceive how full of interest that scene would have been to an intelligent Neptunian, and how eagerly he would have watched the manœuvres of either army, and also, what neither army knew of, the approach of Blucher with his Prussians. Yet, while our Neptunian would thus have traced the progress of the battle from his distant world, the conflict would in reality have been long since decided, the final charge of the British army accomplished, the Imperial Guard destroyed, Napoleon fugitive, and the Prussians, who to the Neptunian would be seen still struggling through muddy roads toward the field of battle, would be relentlessly pursuing the scattered army of France.

It is, however, when we pass beyond the limits of the solar system that the non-contemporaneous nature of the scene presented to us becomes most striking. Here we have to deal not with seconds, minutes, or hours, but with years, decades, and centuries. From the nearest of the fixed stars light takes fully three years in travelling to the earth. Even the star 61 Cygni is so far from us that its light only reaches us in ten years. And, so far as observation has hitherto gone, it seems unlikely that, amid the whole host of heaven, there are so many as a hundred stars—lucid or telescopic—whose light reaches us in a shorter interval of time than twelve or fifteen years. Whatever views we form as to the arrangement of the sidereal scheme, whether those usually accepted be held to be correct, or whether I have been right in adopting others, there can be no doubt that, among the stars revealed to us by the telescope, there must be myriads which lie many times further from us than the bright star in Centaurus and the orb in Cygnus which have been found relatively so near to us. In fact, the views I have adopted, respecting the wide range of magnitude among the fixed stars, do not interfere in the least with the theories which have been formed as to the distances from beyond which the light of some of the stars, only just visible in powerful telescopes, must be supposed to reach us. On the contrary, one may conceive, according to my views, that some of these faintly-seen orbs may be many times larger even than giant Sirius, in which case the distance of such stars would be many times greater than has been hitherto supposed. We may at any rate assume with confidence that many stars only visible in powerful telescopes shine from beyond depths which light would occupy thousands of years in traversing. I cannot, indeed, go further, as astronomers have hitherto done, and say that the nebulæ must be regarded as external galaxies, and therefore as sending their light to us over spaces which light must take many times as long an interval in traversing as it does in travelling to us from the bounds of our own galaxy. But it would be to misinterpret altogether the views which I have formed respecting the universe to suppose that I imagine those distant spaces which astronomers have hitherto filled with imaginary galaxies to be untenanted. On the contrary, I have no doubt whatever that galaxies, resembling our own, exist at distances infinitely exceeding those at which astronomers have placed their most distant nebular universes, if even the bounds of our own galaxy do not extend into space as far as

the widest limits hitherto assigned to the system of
nebulæ. So that I am not precluded from speaking
of orbs whose light, though unrecognized by us, yet
is ever pouring in upon the earth, conveying, though
in letters we cannot decipher, or even trace, a message which has taken millions on millions of years
in traversing the awful gulf beyond which lie those
mysterious realms.

If we conceive, then, that man's visual powers
could suddenly be so increased that, without instrumental aid, he could look around him into the celestial depths, piercing even to those outer galaxies
which astronomers have seen only imaged in the
nebulæ, how wide would be the range of time presented to him by the wonderful scene he would
behold. There would blaze out Alpha Centauri with
its record three years old; there the star in Cygnus
as it existed ten years since; the whole host of stars
known to man would exhibit records ranging from
a few years to many centuries in age; and, lastly, the
external galaxies, which are perhaps forever hidden
from the searching gaze of man, would reveal themselves as they were ages on ages before man appeared upon the earth, ages even before this earth
was framed into a globe, nay ages perhaps before the
planetary system had begun to gather into worlds
around its central orb.

It is when we are thus contemplating in imagination the whole expanse of the universe, and, as one
may almost say, the whole range of past time, that
the author of the little treatise I have spoken of

invites us to consider two processes of thought having sole reference to this earth on which we live,
and to that history which, though all-important to
ourselves, seems to fade into such utter insignificance in the presence of the grand history of the
orbs which lie in uncounted millions around us.

To a being placed on some far-distant orb, whence
light would occupy thousands of years to wing its
flight to us, there would be presented, if he turned
his gaze upon our earth, and if his vision were adequate to tell him of her aspect, the picture of events
which thousands of years since really occurred upon
her surface. For the light which left the earth at
that time, winging its way through space with the
account, if we may so speak, of those occurrences,
is now travelling as swiftly as when it left our earth,
but amid regions of space removed from us by a
light-journey thousands of years in duration. And
thus, to the observer on this distant orb, the events
which happened in those far-off years would seem
to be actually in progress.

But now conceive that powers of locomotion com-
mensurate with his wonderful powers of vision were
given to this being, and that in an instant of time
he could sweep through the enormous interval separating him from our earth, until he were no further
from us than the moon. At the beginning of that
tremendous journey he would be watching events
which were occurring thousands of years since; at its
close he would gaze upon the earth as it was one
second only before he undertook his instantaneous

flight; so that, in the course of his journey, he would gaze upon a succession of events which had occurred during those thousands of years upon the face of this little earth.

The other conception is no less beautiful and striking—I may remark, also, that it is, in a scientific sense, somewhat more exact. Suppose that a being armed with such powers of vision as we have imagined should watch from the neighborhood of our earth the progress of some interesting event. If he then began to travel from the earth at a rate equal to that at which light travels, he would see one phase of the event continually present before him, because he would always be where the light-message recording that event was actually travelling. By passing somewhat less swiftly away, he would see the event taking place with singular slowness; while by passing away more swiftly he would see the event occurring in inverted order. Suppose, for example, he were watching the battle of Waterloo, he could gaze on the fine picture presented by the Imperial Guard as they advanced upon the English army, for hours, years, nay, for centuries or cycles; or he might watch the whole progress of the charge occurring so slowly that years might elapse between each step of the advancing column, and the bullets which mowed down their ranks might either seem unmoving, or else appear to wend their way with scarcely perceptible motion through the air; or, finally, he might so wing his flight through space that the Guard would seem to retreat, their dead men com-

ing to life as the bullets passed from their wounds,
until at length the Old Guard would be seen as it
was when it began its advance, in the assured hope
of deciding Waterloo, as it had decided so many
hard-fought battles for its imperial chief.

It may seem hypercritical to notice scientific in-
exactness in ideas professedly fanciful. But as the
author lays some little stress upon the scientific truth
of the method in which his fancies are exhibited, and
as, further, he dwells upon two of the more obvious
objections to the first conception, it may be well to
consider a further objection, which enforces on us a
total change in the way of presenting the idea. He
remarks that the being he has conceived to be borne
toward the earth through a distance so enormous,
would not see in a moment the whole history of the
earth during the thousands of years considered, but
only the history of that hemisphere which was turned
toward him; while, further, all that took place under
roofs or under cover of any sort would remain unperceived by him. But there is a more serious objection. Among the events which have taken place
during those thousands of years, have been thousands
of revolutions of this earth around the sun, and more
than three hundred and sixty-five times as many rotations of this earth upon her axis, to say nothing of
the stately sway of the earth in her motion of pre-
cession. So that our imaginary observer would in
reality see the earth whirling with inconceivable rapidity upon its axis, and sweeping with even more
tremendous velocity around the sun, so as to com-

plete thousands of circuits in a single second. He would see clouds forming and vanishing in an amazing succession of changes, all occurring in a single instant. And, even though his powers of vision enabled him to pierce the cloud-envelope, he would not have a consecutive presentment of the various events occurring in any part of the earth, but only a haphazard succession of half days for each portion of her surface.

However, we can easily see that, by a slight modification, the beautiful conception of our author can be made to illustrate one mode at least in which the events occurring upon our earth may be conceived to be at all times present to the thoughts of the Almighty. Imagine a sphere with a radius over which light would travel in the time which has elapsed since living creatures first began to move upon this earth, and having for centre the place occupied by the earth at that instant. Then, if we imagine millions of eyes over the surface of that sphere, all turned with piercing powers of vision upon the central earth, we see that to these eyes the earth would be presented by the record of light, not as she is now, but as she was at that primeval day. Now, conceive these millions of eyes closing swiftly in upon the earth, but with this peculiarity of movement that, instead of being always on a sphere around a fixed point, they were always on a sphere around the position which was really occupied by the earth, when the light-messages started which those eyes are receiving at the moment. Then if that

wondrous sphere contracted in an instant, according
to the law assigned it, until its myriad millions of
eyes were gazing intently on our earth from a sphere
of but a few thousand miles in radius, the whole history of the earth, so far as light could render it,
would have been in a moment of time presented
before the myriad-eyed sphere.

To apply this illustration to the subject we are
upon. We know that the Almighty is present where
the boundary of our great sphere was placed at first.
Before Him the light-messages are presenting the account of the primeval earth. He also is present
everywhere within the region through which the contracting sphere was conceived to pass. He therefore
sees the whole history of the earth as presented by
the light-waves. We begin, however, already to feel
that we cannot say of Him what we said of the imaginary being first thought of, or of the myriad-eyed
contracting sphere, that in a moment of time He can
see the whole history of the earth *successively* presented before Him. As He exists throughout that
space, there is no succession of time in His vision
of the events transpiring on our globe. Past and
present are one before Him; and we shall soon see
that present and future also must be one in His
sight.

But now, still considering only the information
which light conveys as it travels onward through
space, we see that what is true of our earth is true
also of every orb throughout the universe. The
whole light-history of every such orb must be pres-

ent at every instant of time to the Creator who is
omnipresent. So that to the obvious conception that
God, being everywhere, must be cognizant of all
things, we have to add this further consequence of
His omnipresence, that He must be cognizant of the
history of all things, in the same sense that a man
is cognizant of events which are passing before his
eyes.

And, by extending these considerations to other
modes in which the history of an event is recorded,
so to speak, by natural processes, we can see that a
much more complete and definite picture of past
events than light can convey must be at all times
present before the Almighty. A sense which could
analyze heat-impressions as eyesight analyzes light,
would tell us not only what eyesight tells us, but
much that no light-messages can convey to us. At
least it is conceivable that a sense of this sort would
enable the being provided with it to recognize not
merely the nature of the surface of any body whose
heat reached the organ of this sense, but the quality
of the body's internal structure, processes going on
within the body, or the nature of bodies so placed
that eyesight would not render us sensible even of
their existence. Electricity, in like manner, would
avail to give information altogether distinct from that
which light can impart. And precisely as, in considering light, we saw that the Creator must be supposed sensible of every light-record travelling through
space, so, as regards these imaginary but conceivable
senses, we must believe that any information which

they could by any possibility impart must be conveyed to the omnipresent God. And, further, it would be a contradiction to our belief in His infinite wisdom to suppose that the infinite multiplicity of the records thus continually present before Him could in any way render their significance less distinct.[1]

But, turning from the consideration that the Almighty, by virtue of His omnipresence, is thus cognizant, not merely of all that is at any moment taking place throughout the universe, but of all that has taken place in the infinity of past time, we have to consider another mode in which the universe must be regarded as present before Almighty God.

The senses by which we judge of what is going on around us are, after all, merely one means by which we judge of causes by their effects. When we say, for instance, that we have seen such and such an object, or watched such and such an event, what we really imply is, that we have recognized certain physical impressions, which we can only ex-

---

[1] Moralizing may seem altogether out of place in such a work as this, but certainly one is tempted to dwell somewhat thoughtfully on the ideas raised by the considerations I have dwelt on above. It is not without a feeling of awe that one considers that the records of every action of our lives are not merely at this moment before God, but will for ever and ever be freshly present to Him: and *that*, not merely in the sense that He knows everything (an idea too vague for man rightly to grasp), but by the action of physical processes such as our Faradays and Tyndalls deal with. May it not be through an instinctive recognition of this great truth that man alone, of all the creatures which people this earth, feels contrition for long-past misdeeds, even where he has no fear of their ever bearing fruit in future sorrows?

plain by the existence of that object, or by the
occurrence of that event. We know, in fact, that
in certain exceptional cases impressions resembling
those caused by the actual presence of an object, or
by the actual occurrence of some event, may arise
where no such object has been present, or where no
such event has transpired. Still, we commonly feel
safe from error, in concluding, from certain impressions conveyed to the mind by the agency of the
visual organs, that certain objects have been really
present, at rest or in action, before us.

But, then, even man, limited as are his powers,
can yet follow a series of effects and causes far more
numerous than those concerned in the act of vision;
and so he can become certain of the occurrence of
past events of which no sense he possesses gives him
any direct information. For example, though I
neither saw the battle of Waterloo nor heard the
thunder of the guns there, yet I am as certain that
the battle really took place as though sight and hearing had given me direct information on the matter.
And, when I inquire whence that certainty arises, I
find a complicated series of events involved in my
acquisition of the knowledge that the battle took
place. My interpretation of the letter-press account
of the battle involved in itself a number of more or
less complex relations, associated with the question
of my confidence in those who taught me that certain symbols represented certain letters, that certain
combinations of letters represented certain words, and
that certain words represented certain ideas. Not to

follow out the long train of ideas thus suggested, it will be clear that, with regard to a variety of matters, the knowledge which any man has is associated with considerations of cause and effect, of general experience, of confidence in the accounts of others or in his own judgment, which are in reality of a highly-complex character.

Now, we are led by these thoughts to remember that, independently of those records of past events which are brought continually before the Almighty by processes resembling those which directly affect our senses, such events must be recognizable by Him (even to their minutest details) in the consequences which they have led to. If a great naturalist like Huxley or Owen can tell, by examining the tooth of a creature belonging to some long-extinct race, not only what the characteristics of that race were, but the general nature of the scenery amid which such creatures lived, we see at once that a single grain of sand or drop of water must convey to the Omniscient the history of the whole world of which it forms part. Nay, why should we pause here? The history of that world is in truth bound up so intimately with the history of the universe, that the grain of sand or drop of water conveys not only the history of a world, but with equal completeness the history of the whole universe.

The Almighty, then, by virtue of His possessing in an infinite degree that quality which enables man to reason upon past events of which his senses bring him no direct intelligence, has the whole past history of the universe continually present before Him, in the state and position of each single atom throughout infinity of space.[1]

Turning from the past to the future, we must not let the limited nature of our recognition of the course of future events prevent us from forming a just opinion as to the way in which the future must be always present before God. We can judge of the past by its effects, but we are almost utterly unable to judge of the future by its causes. Yet we cannot doubt that the future *is* present in its germs, precisely as the past is present in its fruits. It may be regarded in fact as merely a peculiarity of man's constitution that the past is more clearly present to his mental vision than the future. It is easy not only to conceive that the future and the past should be equally present to intelligent creatures, but to conceive of a form of intelligence according to which past events would be obliterated from the mind as fast as they took place, while the future should be as actually present as to the ordinary human mind the past is.

In considering the Omniscient, however, all questions of degree must be set on one side. The future must be as absolutely and essentially present to Him in its germs as the past has been shown to be in its

---

[1] In fact, if we consider the matter attentively, we see that there cannot be a single atom throughout space which could have attained its present exact position and state, had the history of any part of the universe, however insignificant, been otherwise than it has actually been, in even the minutest degree.

fruits. If a grain of sand contains in its state, figure, and position, the picture of the universe as it
is, and the whole history of the universe throughout
the infinite past—and who can doubt that this is so?
—it contains with equal completeness the history of
the universe throughout the infinite future. No
other view is compatible with the assumption of
the Almighty's infinite wisdom, and no assumption
which limits the wisdom of God is compatible with
our belief that He is supreme in the universe.

Obviously also every *event*, however trifling, must
be held to contain in itself the whole history of the
universe throughout the infinite past, and throughout
the infinite future. For every event, let its direct
importance be what it may, is indissolubly bound up
with events preceding, accompanying, and following
it, in endless series of causation, interaction, and
effect.

So far, then, as the Almighty's watch over His
universe is concerned, we have two lines of thought,
each leading to the recognition of a perfect supervision. In virtue (1) of His omnipresence, and (2) of
His infinite wisdom, He sees at each instant the
whole universe as it has been in the infinite past,
as it is now, and as it will be in the infinite future;
and this being as true of any one instant as it is of
any other, we recognize the operation of yet a new
form of infinity—the infinite duration of the Almighty's existence—to render yet more inconceivably perfect God's supervision of His universe.

And now with regard to control. Does the Almighty, who supervises all things, exercise any controlling action upon the course of events?

It need hardly be said that, if God does exercise control, apart from the laws which He has assigned to His universe, His knowledge of the progress of past and future events is not therefore to be called in question, since His own direct action, whether in the past or in the future, is quite as much the subject of His consciousness (to use this word for want of a better) as the action of His creatures or of the laws He has primarily set them.

We know that certain laws have been assigned to the universe, and we know also that, so far as our very limited experience enables us to determine, these laws are never abrogated.[1] Here I set alto-

---

[1] All things working thus according to law, however, certain difficulties suggest themselves which must not be left undealt with, since not to consider them might be to leave painful doubts in the minds of some who may read these pages.

In the first place, there is the old question of the relation between man's free-will and the absolute foreknowledge of Almighty God. It seems clear to many that if all things are foreknown there can be no such thing as free-will; insomuch that some have even felt forced to believe that the Almighty, though undoubtedly omniscient, must in a sense forego His knowledge of future events so that the actions of men may be subject to the control of their will. But in reality we have only to consider the analogy of human foreknowledge, to see that there is no necessity for any theory so self-contradictory as this. We have already considered other attributes of the Almighty as in a sense resembling, though infinitely exceeding in range of action, certain attributes of man; let us, then, inquire whether that attribute of man which, though imperfect and limited, yet corresponds to the foreknowledge of God, affords us any reason for believing that perfect foreknowledge bars the exercise of free-will. The answer is obvious at once. We know that we often judge, with more or less certainty of conviction, that such and such acts will be performed by others, and that yet our anticipation in no sense influences the will of

gether aside, for the moment, the possibility of miracles, and consider only the results of experimental
or observational science. Thus, we are led to the
conclusion that all things happen according to set

---

the persons who are expected so to act. Suppose I remember, for example, that I have left a valuable in a room which will presently be passed
through by one whom I know to be dishonest; I judge accordingly that
the person will purloin the valuable. In this case his free-will is not
affected- by my anticipation; nor would it be though a yet clearer conviction of his conduct were impressed upon me. There is, in fact, no conceivable degree of certainty on my part which would render him unde-
serving of punishment for stealing the valuable. And so, not to give
further instances where the matter is so obvious, we see that no conceivable degree of foreknowledge bars free-will. The infinite and absolute
foreknowledge of the Almighty is therefore altogether dissociated from the
dangerous and hurtful belief in a predestination which renders man irre-
sponsible for his actions.

Secondly, the belief in the absolute perfection of the laws according to
which God rules His universe, insomuch that throughout all the worlds
in space all things work according to those laws without need of special
interference on His part, has been thought by many, and is painfully felt
by some, to oppose itself to our belief in the efficacy of prayer. In touch-
ing on this point, I wish very carefully to avoid any intrusion on matters
apart from the general scope of my subject; but a few words may be permitted me on a point which comes close home to the hearts of all of us,
and which also does seem in a sense associated with the matters I have
been dealing with. All men, I suppose, pray; though many may in words
deride prayer, and though hundreds, without expressing doubts, may fail
to see any possible utility in the practice, because they cannot believe
that the action of the physical laws of God can be interfered with in answer to the appeal of His creatures. It is because I fear lest some of my
readers should have felt this difficulty, and should find their doubts confirmed by anything I may here have written, that I indicate the explanation which I suppose every one who thinks much upon this point would
probably be led to. Remembering that, on the one hand, it is unreasonable to conceive that God would have allowed a belief in the efficacy of
prayer to grow, as it has done, to be a part of human nature, were that
belief founded in a monstrous fiction, and that, on the other hand, it is
unreasonable to suppose that physical laws are interfered with in response
to the millions of prayers daily offered by men, the obvious conclusion
seems to be that prayers are responded to (where it has seemed fitting that

physical laws: and without, by any means, adopting the view that the Almighty exercises no special control over His universe, we see strong reason to believe that the laws which He has assigned to it are

---

they should be) without interference with natural laws; that, in fact, the scheme of the Almighty includes at once the prayers and their response. It seems baffling, indeed, to human thoughts that such an infinity of varied interests should thus be provided for, in a scheme whose extent covers the infinity of past and future time; but where infinite wisdom is in question this consideration need not trouble us. Nor is this particular mode of control inconsistent even with our merely human conceptions of what is reasonable. For instance, a father, desirous at once of testing and rewarding the obedience of a son, might tell him to go to such a place and to open such a box, having beforehand placed therein a reward for his son's obedience. Here the fulfilment of the father's request would no more result in bringing the gift to the box, than our fulfilment of the duty of prayer can cause the laws of Nature to cease or change in their operation; yet obedience would in the one case, as we can conceive it does in the other, in reality bring about its own reward. And, further, it may be remarked that, precisely as the greater or less certainty of the father as to his son's obedience would in no sense affect the latter's merit, so neither does the absolute foreknowledge of God as to the prayers which His creatures will offer up, affect in any sense the merit which He has been pleased to recognize in the sincere performance of the act of prayer.

Lastly, there is the difficulty as to our belief in miracles—that is, in events which involve the temporary suspension or alteration of natural laws. It must be remembered here that recent physical researches, though they have enabled us to interpret so many of the laws of Nature, yet tell neither for nor against our recognition of the possibility of miracles. It belongs to the very essence of a miracle that it should be an event which no physical researches can explain, or indeed can affect otherwise than to render it the more inexplicable. The question is, not whether such and such an event is more or less wonderful to the unlearned Hodge or Styles on the one part, or to a Newton or a Faraday on the other, but whether an event can really take place in which the laws of Nature have absolutely been annulled and abrogated. I take it, for instance, that if we could see a hungry multitude fed with a few loaves, and were absolutely certain that so many thousands had been satisfied with what would naturally be the food but of a few, our wonder would not be greater or less whether we viewed the matter as a laborer would, who simply knows what hunger is and what is needed to satisfy

sufficient for the control of all things. Indeed, so far as all things take place in accordance with laws which the Almighty must assuredly have Himself ordained, we may say that every event which has happened or will happen throughout infinite time is the direct work, and indicates the direct purpose and

---

it, or whether we were familiar with the analysis of bread and comparted the amount of fibrine and albumen contained in the loaves with what we knew of the daily or hourly exhaustion of the corresponding materials in the human frame.

The arguments in favor of miracles or against their having occurred (of their possibility there need be no question) are the same now as they were in less scientific ages. Those who believe in the occurrence of miracles argue thus: Man differs from all other terrestrial creatures in being responsible to his Creator. Thus between him and Almighty God there is a direct relation, which renders it necessary that the will of God should be communicated to man. Now, we can conceive no way in which such communication can be made in an unmistakable manner, but by events which involve an unmistakable exercise of a power belonging to God alone —that is, by events of a supernatural character. The believer in miracles further argues that nothing tending to prove the impossibility (in a natural sense) of an event of this sort can be accepted to disprove its occurrence, since what is essentially requisite to the very purpose of a miracle is that it should be in a natural sense impossible. Nor is it necessary that any recorded miracle should be in itself of a striking or imposing character, so long as its connection with the communication of God's will in a special manner is reasonably established, since the triviality or non-triviality of an event whose miraculous character is in question is to be judged only by the circumstances of those for whose instruction the miracle is supposed to have been worked.

The argument against the occurrence of miracles has been already considered. As has been pointed out, it not only does not meet the argument just stated, but rests on the very fact which constitutes the basis of that argument—the fact, namely, that the occurrence of miracles is contrary to experience. It is obvious, then, that the considerations I have urged, as to the nature of God's control over His universe, need not be regarded as in the slightest degree affecting the belief of men in those direct relations between God and man which have been held to involve the necessity of miracles. To speak further, however, on this matter would bring me to deal with that subject which I have selected to avoid.

will, of Almighty God. Nor need the thought that the Almighty thus seems to be made the author of evil as well as of good in any way startle us, because we know that what constitutes evil or good in our limited vision may by no means be accepted as indicative of what is evil or good as the work of God. *We* know, limited as our wisdom is, that evil often works to good, so that if the Almighty, whose wisdom extends over the never-ending chain of sequent events, seems, by permitting evil, to, in a sense, countenance it, we are to recognize the sequent good as in truth His work, and to regard that which is objectively evil (and actually evil in the creature who does it) as subjectively good in Him who permits it with a perfect knowledge of all that in the infinity of future time is to flow from it.

Now, it seems conceivable that in reality it is only our limited acquaintance with the operation of the laws which God has set His universe, which makes us regard them as unchanging, and, so to speak, inexorable. There seems, indeed, reason rather to expect than to deny, that He who made the laws may annul or suspend them at His pleasure.

But I think that this view—though it has been entertained by many thoughtful men, especially because it seems to give the Almighty a special controlling power over His universe—is in reality inconsistent with just conceptions of His infinite wisdom. If His wisdom, though inconceivably great, were yet finite, we could not suppose that the universe would have been so planned (still to use inexact words for want of better), and laws of such a nature assigned to it, that throughout the infinity of time all things should work out the will and purpose of Almighty God. There would then, undoubtedly, be continual need of adaptation, change, remodelling—of the annulment of a law here, or its suspension there—in order that the whole might not fall to wrack. But where the God of Nature is infinitely wise, there can be no such necessity. The whole scheme of the universe must needs be so perfect that direct intervention cannot at any time be required.

To sum up, we find ourselves led to the belief that, while intervention with the operation of natural laws is unnecessary, all the worlds existing throughout space are, in a very definite and special manner, watched over and controlled by an omnipresent, omnipotent, and omniscient Being; that before Him the infinite past and the infinite future of the universe are at all times sensibly present; that each the minutest atom and every the least important event exhibits *before Him at each instant the perfect history of the limitless past and future of the universe; and lastly, that His infinitely perfect consciousness of, and control over, all that has been, is, or will be, are infinitely multiplied (to use the only available expression) by the infinite duration throughout which His existence extends.

THE END